OSTRI
FARMING

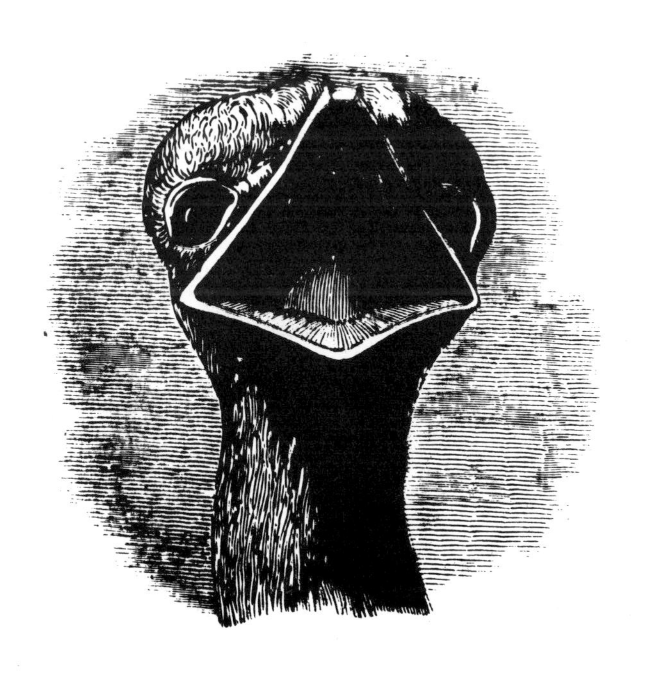

Books on Commercial Aspects of Farming

The publishers have many books on the commercial or hobby aspects of keeping poultry, rabbits, ducks, geese, turkeys, guinea fowl, chinchillas and other stock. Readers wanting information on these subjects, as well as on cage and aviary birds, should write for details.

OSTRICH FARMING

JOSEPH BATTY

Beech Publishing House

© J Batty, 1994

This book is copyright and may not be reproduced or copied in any way without the express permission of the publishers in writing.

First Edition 1994
New Impression 1995

ISBN 1-85736-042-7

Beech Publishing House
The Bindery
Sawmill Buildings
Stedham, Midhurst,
West Sussex GU29 ONY

Contents

Foreword

This book was written because of the many requests received by the publisher for an introduction to ostrich farming. There are many other authors who are more capable of dealing with the technicalities of ostrich farming; ie, the ostrich farmers themselves. Alas, despite trying to secure the services of an ostrich farmer as an author there were no takers and so the task fell to me. Fortunately, except for the size, the keeping of ostriches is very little different from keeping laying hens, ducks, geese or turkeys of which I have kept and bred over many years.

The main source of information on ostrich farming is South Africa where it was pioneered and still goes on. Many books were written on the subject at the end of the last century. A number of these I have been able to locate through libraries and have been used as background information.

The South African Embassy also supplied details. In addition, information was gathered from ostrich farmers and suppliers of foodstuffs. Many sources were extremely helpful.

Special mention should be mentioned of the study conducted by Dr Brian Bertram for the RSPCA on Welfare Standards for ostrich farming (see Bibliography). This has been published at an opportune time and quite clearly the Government should address the difficult problem of killing ostriches for human consumption. A number of birds do not reach the standard required for breeding or feathers and therefore these 'wasters' must be marketed to make ostrich farming commercially viable.

I trust the work stimulates interest in this long established practice of ostrich farming. Moreover, it is hoped that the proper emphasis will be given to the welfare aspects and facilities provided will meet strict standards.

J Batty

Figure 0.1 Features of the Ostrich

1
INTRODUCTION

BRIEF EARLY HISTORY

OSTRICH farming was at one time one of the most flourishing, lucrative, and interesting industries in Cape Colony, South Africa. The birds were bred and raised to meet the requirements of the fashion industry which used enormous numbers of feathers to adorn hats and other wearing apparel. However, the demand declined and , as a result, so did the industry. Today numbers are relatively small.

Up to 1914 the development of ostrich farming was booming , a process started around 1870 in the Oudtshoorn District in South Africa. In the early 1880s there were more than 100,000 birds which continued to increase until around a million birds were being farmed. Then as feathers became 'out of fashion' , as decoration for ladies' hats and other garments, there was a rapid decline and the millionaire farmers found their riches disappearing and the flocks of birds were reduced. Today the figure of around 100,000 appears to be the likely total in existence.

There were also stocks in Australia and various other countries and, again, there was a marked decline, sometimes birds being released into the wild. In much more recent times ostrich farming has been taken up in Israel and in the UK and other European countries. Interest is also being shown in North America, particularly in the USA.

MORE DETAILED HISTORY

Although it is acknowledged that South Africa was responsible for developing **ostrich farming** there should be awareness of the part also played by other countries. Indeed, well before 1870 ostriches were kept in enclosures in various parts of Africa.

The *Acclimatisation Society of Paris* in 1859, recognizing that the plumes required could not depend on wild stock, offered prizes for the successful farming of ostriches in Senegal and Algeria and success went to the latter, the recipient being a Mr M Hardy at Hamma.

Success was also recorded in Italy when Prince Demidoff was successful in 1859 in rearing two chicks and the following year others were hatched. This first European achievement was followed by others in Marseilles, Grenoble, and Madrid.

In South Africa the first successful hatching took place in 1866 and young birds were reared in 1870, the starting date referred to on the preceding page.

Early References

There are many references to ostriches from very early times. The bird was known from many sources. In the bible there are examples in **Job** and **Jeremiah**. Apparently the ostrich was regarded as being of little intelligence being careless with her eggs and her young.

In ancient literature from Egypt, Greece and Rome there are many references which show the regard paid to the beauty of the feathers. In Egyptology the feathers are mentioned as *shoo* and there was an illustration of an ostrich in a sepulchral chamber of the 18th dynasty. The feather, because it is evenly balanced, was regarded as a symbol of justice by the Egyptians.

PRACTICAL USES OF THE OSTRICH

There are many practical uses attributed to the ostrich throughout history. The modern uses are not far removed from many of these. Examples are as follows:

1. Skins used for garments and shields.

2. Flesh taken as a food.

Generally the older birds would be tough and rather hard to digest. On the domesticated ostrich, fed well and not allowed to gallop around, the meat is very palatable.

3. Used as transport.

The ladies of ancient Rome were said to favour riding on ostriches and it is said that Queen Arsinoe of Egypt had a statue made showing her riding an ostrich. The natives of Africa still ride the ostrich. An ostrich has also been used to pull a small 'trap' or cart.

In the UK the RSPCA* recommend that ostriches should not be used as 'horses' and certainly there is merit in this recommendation for rider as well as the bird.

4. Use of the plumes or feathers.

In ancient times the ostrich plumes were used by men to wear in their helmets; there is a record as early as BC 425 in Greece. The nobles of England also used feathers in their black velvet caps as early as the 14th century. Even Royalty used the plumes and the badge of the Prince of Wales had three ostrich feathers from quite early times.

The adornment of ladies hats and other apparel is relatively modern. In ancient times ladies did not wear hats and therefore had no need to embellish them. It was only when the hat or bonnet became a recognized article of wear that the feathers became popular for this purpose.

* ***Welfare Standards for the humane farming of ostriches in the United Kingdom*** **, RSPCA & Brian Bertram, 1993**

Importance of Location

There main factors in establishing ostrich farming in South Africa were as follows:

1. Existence of wild birds.
2. A population which understood the ostrich and its habits.
3. The climate and soil suitable for producing lucerne, a special type of grass which is fed to the birds.
4. The introduction of an incubator suitable for hatching ostrich eggs , thus allowing the ostrich population to increase considerably.

An early incubator by A Douglass is illustrated, showing how much thought had gone into the problems of hatching these very large eggs. Rearing chicks is also a serious problem and therefore methods had to be developed which gave satisfactory results.

SELECTION OF THE BEST

In Ostrich farming, as in the breeding of all other kinds of live stock, it only pays to keep the best; therefore it is most important that the stock selected at the start should be of the very best quality. High-class birds cost no more to keep than inferior ones, and their produce is infinitely more profitable. More expensive, original breeding stock may be repaid over and over again in the first season or two. There is a vast difference in the quality of meat and feathers produced by different strains; over the years ostriches have developed and improvements have been made; also 'hybrids' have been produced by carefully selecting the different strains and breeding from them. Therefore the best stock birds might cost more initially but in the long run will be a better proposition.

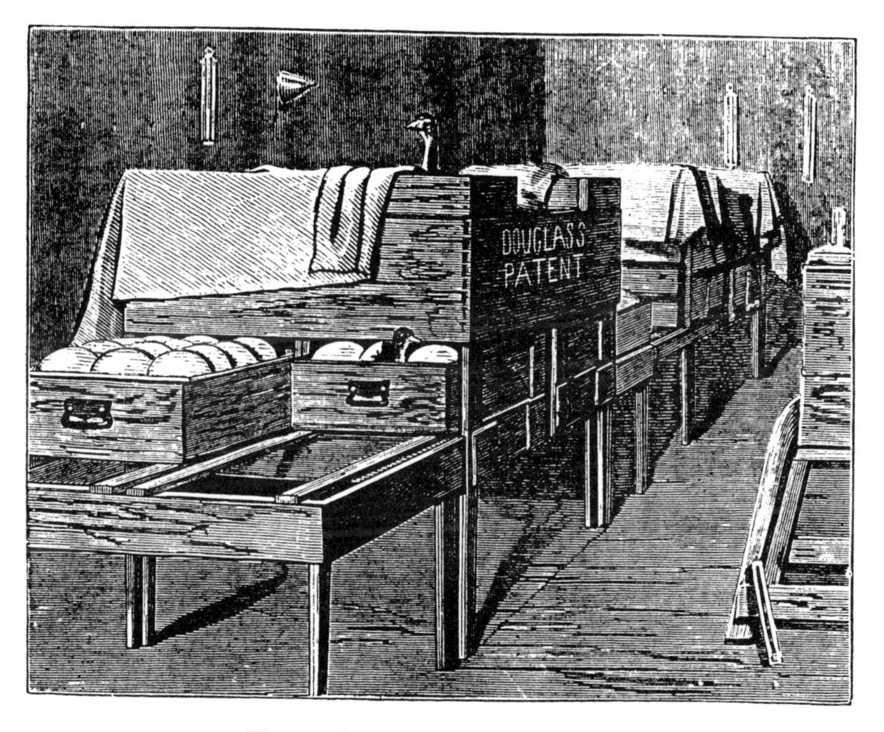

Figure 1.1 Early Incubators
(shown to indicate the importance attached to leveloping a successful machine in the early days of ostrich farming; said to be the main reason for the expansion of the industry; developed in 1869 by Mr Arthur Douglass, a farmer in South Africa)

Pedigree is as important in a family of Ostriches as it is in racehorses. Therefore it is imperative that the beginner should not commence his buying until he has given full consideration to all aspects and has learnt from those who know something of the value of different strains or families of birds. Pedigree, certainly, is not everything, but it is a very great deal, and when valuable properties and pedigree go together in the same bird, the purchaser is not likely to repent of his bargain, where as looks without pedigree, or pedigree without good looks may result in nothing but disappoint-ment, vexation and loss.

First-class birds will pay, pay well, and pay quickly, but poor ones never. A mistake at the start is a serious matter, therefore we strongly urge readers of this book to think well before they invest their money in stock. Entered upon carelessly, ostrich farming may mean failure, but if judgment and careful thought are given to it then he who be-comes an ostrich farmer may make a good living. Prices vary according to circumstances, but they are more fixed now than a few years ago, and speaking generally a high-class pair of *young* birds for future breeding should cost around £1,500 the pair. Cheaper birds may be found, but they may not have the potential to grow to the desired weight.

POTENTIAL FOR PROFIT

The potential for profit arises from the following :

1. Breeding young stock for resale.

2. Raising birds for meat.

3. Using the feathers for fashion or industry. (this is a potential to be developed -- yet at present there seems little hope for a fashion revival in feathers because the climate of opinion is against the exploitation of birds or animals).

4. Selling eggs for hatching.

5.Providing 'know how' on a consultancy basis.

6. Selling decorated ostrich eggs to tourists and others such as educational establishments.

7. Using the eggs for eating. (An ostrich egg is the equivalent of 24 normal hen eggs so scrambled egg from one egg will feed a large family). However, a fertile egg is quite valuable and is not likely to be used or sold for culinary purposes unless there is a glut.

8. Producing leather for making high quality goods, such as wallets and handbags.

These possibilities are examined in more detail later. Undoubtedly they still exist and the use of feathers in industry for dusting, polishing and other uses will provide a market for the surplus.

With all enterprises involving livestock it will be essential to build up a sound nucleus of breeding stock. Accordingly, any birds that do not meet with established criteria should be culled and used to earn money to keep the enterprise afloat until many head of parent stock are available for breeding. It has been suggested that only around 20% will be bred which will be first class for breeding. These should be sound in all physical characteristics, without any signs of disease. Remember, without top class parents, the progeny is likely to be weak, possessing all the same faults that existed in the first place.

THE MAIN PROBLEMS

Undoubtedly, the potential for ostrich farming in the UK is quite large, but there are likely to be problems. These are as follows:

1. Shortage of parent stock in this country and abroad.

A mature breeding pair is likely to cost in excess of £10,000* which is not excessive when we consider the cost of establishing a pedigree herd of cattle or other animals, but nevertheless, if around 30 pairs are to be obtained (a reasonable size flock for starting a farm), the total livestock cost is substantial.

2. Suitable buildings, fencing and grazing land are essential.

Again the investment will be substantial, but existing farmers may run ostrich farming with some other operation, thus making the proposition viable in the early, development stages.

3. Land suitable for growing Lucerne.

The deep fertile soil for lucerne is an essential requirement and would not be available generally. More detail is given on this aspect in a later chapter.

4. Overcoming Climatic difficulties.

Ostriches are quite hardy and will adapt readily to an indifferent climate. However, chicks should not be exposed to damp, cold weather or they

---

***Prices quoted should be taken with caution. During the period of writing this book (about 2 years) there have been reported large increases. Until the market has settled buy with care and only healthy stock.**

will perish. Special rearing quarters will be necessary and if birds are to be imported a quarantine period in an approved establishment will be essential.

5. Complying with Regulations

Ostriches may be classified as 'wild animals' and will require a special licence to keep them. Enquiries should be made at the appropriate department in the country concerned.

In the UK an application must be made to the local administrative authority which should be straight forward, provided it can be shown that the ostriches are to be kept under suitable conditions. The main purpose of the regulations are to prevent irresponsible individuals from keeping a large creature like an ostrich (largest bird in existence) within the confines of a small garden. In the proper environment ostriches should be no more dangerous than pigs, cattle or horses.

Before venturing into ostrich farming interested parties should obtain an insight into the nature of the bird and what it represents in terms of domesticity. Some have argued that although a bird the ostrich is akin to an animal having a two–toed foot and strong legs on which to run from its enemies. Certainly, there are many unique features which call for special treatments. The next chapter examines in outline the natural history of the ostrich and covers many of these special features.

Figure 1.2 Ostriches Feeding

2
NATURAL HISTORY

Ostrich : *Struthio camelus*

THE RATITES

The ostrich belongs to a group of birds known as *Ratites* ; **birds which have a rounded body, lacking the 'keel' (breast bone), essential for flying**. Because of this characteristic the ostrich must rely on speed to avoid being captured or killed. Fortunately, a high speed is possible with the result that the ostrich can outrun man or animals.The shape of the body structure can be seen from the diagram of a skeleton. (Fig. 2.1)

Ostriches are related to other birds which cannot fly. These include the Emus, Rheas, Cassowaries, and Kiwis. It appears to be only the ostrich which has been domesticated and whilst we see the other species in zoos the potential to farm them does not appear to have been attempted; yet there are reports from early references that the flesh and eggs make excellent food. In the case of the Emu this is a bird of around 6 feet tall and therefore of large proportions. Its flesh is said to resemble beef in parts and chicken in others. They were eaten by the Australian settlers.

In habits the emus are like the ostriches and graze the land eating grass and other vegetation. In domesticity they are also fond of lettuce, cabbages and similar plants. In the laying season the diet should be supplemented with poultry food and a few handfuls of pellets at any time is recommended, especially in a relatively cold climate.

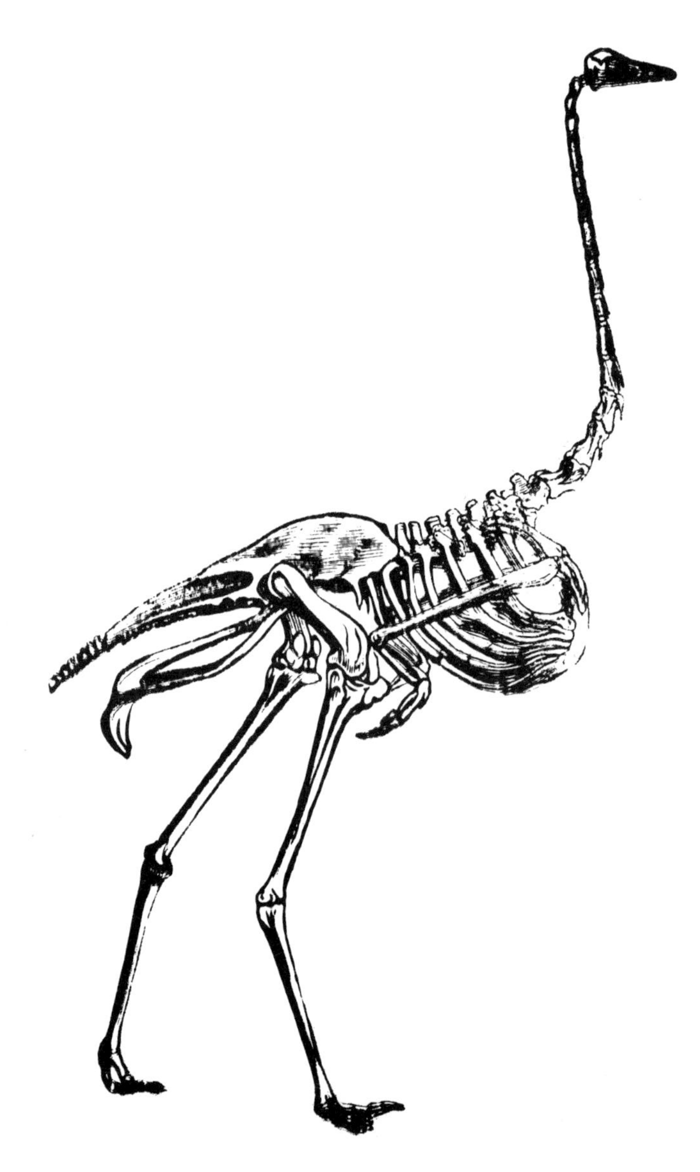

Figure 2.1 Skeleton of Ostrich

THE FAMILY

The ostrich is the only member of a family known as **Struthionidae**. There are 6 species of ostrich as follows :

1.*Struthio camelus australis* ; South West Africa and Angola

2. *S. c. camelus* ; in an area extending from the Niger to Ethiopia.

3. S. c. massaicus ; also known as the Masai ostrich, which is found in Tanzia and Southern Kenya.

4. *S. c. molybdophanes* ; is found in the bush in Somalia, Ethiopia and Northern Kenya.

5. *S. c. spatzi* ; Mauritania and Rio de Oro.

6. *S. c. syricas* ; Syria and Arabia, but possibly now extinct.

The country of origin is regarded as Africa, but it is believed by some that it was also an inhabitant of Asia, including India.Various authorities have commented on the Asian connection.The evidence suggests that ostriches existed in various parts of Asia and India and in the latter country fossils have been found. It must be appreciated that it is at home in the open deserts and plains and not in the dense jungles or forests. In those surroundings it can make use of its very fast speed and outrun predators, including man.

Undoubtedly the ostrich is a bird accustomed to temperate latitudes, where there are areas of dry, well drained land, where the appropriate food can be found. Any climate which gives these conditions is capable of sustaining the ostrich. However, as now shown, even colder climates may be suitable, provided the correct conditions can be created. In warm countries such as Israel and Australia the suitability is obvious.

In the British Isles the winter climate is not really suitable and therefore special care must be taken as covered in the chapters on ostrich farming. Birds adapt to many climates. If we take the domesticated fowl we can trace its origins back to the Jungle Fowl which still inhabit the jungles of India.* There is a similar example with peafowl which have taken to all kinds of climate and breed and thrive out of doors. Even our wild pheasant is a native of warmer lands, but is now just at home in the British countryside as in China and other Asian countries.

CHARACTERISTICS OF THE OSTRICH

The characteristics of the ostrich should be understood by all who are to keep them in some way. The main features are as follows:

1. Camel–like features.

The feet are cloven with well padded soles making them like the camel in its constant battle against the elements of the desert and the moving sand. The legs topped by muscular thighs, denuded of feathers are also suitable for desert life. An ostrich has a large callous pad on its breast and on which it leans when at rest is also like the camel.

2. Bird–like features.

Unlike the camel the ostrich relies on the laying of eggs for reproduction. Accordingly, there must be a male bird and females constantly running together to produce fertile eggs. The basic anatomy, except for the purpose of survival, are those of the bird, although, of course, this bird can never fly. There is the development of the egg within the ovary and the vast quanties of calcium required for the upkeep of the body and the creation of the shells on the very large eggs.

The more important aspects are now examined in more detail.

---

*See *Keeping Jungle Fowl*, J Batty, where the origins are examined.

Loss of Power of Flight

The sheer weight of the ostrich makes flight impossible. If the breast bones of man and various birds are compared it will be seen that an average man would require a breast bone projecting 4ft. to support large enough wing muscles to fly. The ostrich at a weight approaching 300lb (135 k) has no chance of getting off the ground. Instead , it must rely on the strong, muscular legs which can travel at a speed equivalent of up to 40 miles per hour. If and when it ever flew has been debated, but there is no conclusion can be reached; it is difficult to conceive, but under different conditions, with more knowledge on the original form, the matter may be different.

The Foot

The ostrich has only two toes and the inner one has a claw and is much larger than the outer toe. The ancient scholars regarded it as a form of animal and assigned it the name Camel-bird. Aristotle thought it a mixture of beast and bird and Pliny classified as a form of beast. (see Fig 2.2).

Head and Tongue

The ostrich has a strong , straight beak which include the nostrils with the eye set in a small head. In fact, for its size the ostrich has a very small brain and is not intelligent. The tongue is very small and is short and rounded. (see Fig 2.3).

The Legs

The legs are what would be expected from a terrestrial roamer. They are long , strong and muscular with voluminous thighs devoid of feathers. It has been estimated that a bird in full gallop has a stride of 22 to 28 feet being possible by full use of the four joints on the leg giving maximum power. There is recognition that the design of the leg gives what might be described as 'perfect mechanism'.

Figure 2.2 Foot of Ostrich

Somewhat like a camel's foot.

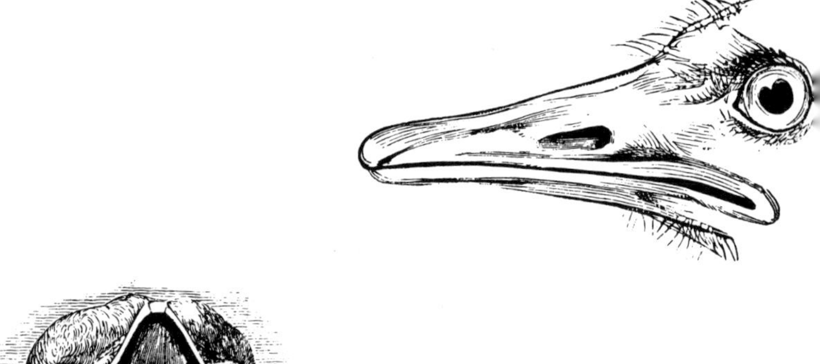

Figure 2.3 *Head of Ostrich --front and side views*

The Stomach

The ostrich is known for its strange eating habits, gobbling anything which looks palatable, with the result that many are injured or killed from the act of eating metal or other man–made objects . However, it does have a very powerful stomach capable of digesting the coarsest vegeta– tion. Accordingly, in the wild all types of vegetation are taken. They eat shoots, fruit, seeds, leaves, creepers, and insects and small lizards and similar creatures. They natu– rally eat small stones for grit and the stomach produces large quantities of acids for digestion.

Unlike what is sometimes suggested the ostrich cannot do without refreshment and it must receive liquid in the form of water, or juices from plants.

The Plumage

The male ostrich is primarily black with white feath– ers in the wings and tail (Ostrich plumes) and the female is a greyish brown. The ostrich lives to a considerable age (possibly 100 years) and continues to produce eggs for about 20 years provided the conditions are appropriate.

More details on this aspect are given in later sections which deal with the practical aspects of ostrich farming.

Breeding

The male ostrich is polygymous and will run with as many as 10 hens, although from two to six is more usual. Each female will lay a number of eggs , which may be from six to twelve. A communal nest may be used with the result that as many as 40 to 60 eggs may be incubated with the result that many do not hatch. Obviously the female will

Figure 2.4,Ostriches and Nest

cover about 15 eggs only so the rest will spoil.

Egg Size

Eggs are quite large, although relatively small for the size of the bird. The length is around 6" (15cm) and the width is 5" (13cm). The weight is around 1,400 grammes. Comparative sizes are (grammes) :

1. Swan 285
2. Peafowl 90
3. Turkey 85
4. Duck 80
5. Fowl 58
6. Canary 2

It will be seen that the larger birds all produce fairly small eggs *compared with body size* . Nevertheless, the ostrich egg is very large and many stories surround its uses; for example:

1. It takes one hour to boil; hard boiled 2 hours, cooked gently.

2. One ostrich egg is the equivalent to 24 normal hen eggs and it is highly flavoured.

3. An omelette is made with cheese and grated onion and is a favourite dish in Oudtshoorn (Centre for ostrich farming in S. Africa).

4. The breaking strength (BS) is 55 kilos and obviously the shell is very thick. A hen egg has a BS of 4 Kilos.

Obviously at today's prices for eggs there may be some reluctance to use the eggs for food, although the practice still goes on in South Africa. Eggs not up to standard for incubation, eg, small, mis-shapen or cracked, may be eaten.

Incubation

The ostrich hen lays around 12 to 15 eggs in a clutch. If the eggs are taken away a hen may lay up to 100 eggs per annum, but the more normal yield is likely to be about 50 eggs.

The male ostrich may have a following of a few hens and once the simple nest is full , the male and what is believed to be the dominant female share the incubation , which lasts about 6 weeks. The male takes the evening and night shifts and the female the day–time. At intervals the eggs are turned , thus avoiding the yolk sticking to the shell and also allowing both sides of the egg to be heated.

Since the nest will be over–filling only the eggs in the centre will be hatched. Sometimes writers suggest that the hatching is really done by the heat of the sun and the sitting birds simply protect the eggs. However, if this were the case many more would hatch -- not just those in the centre, so it would appear that the incubation by the birds is vital. In any event the temperature at night will be much cooler than at daytime so sitting on them during a cool period will be es–sential.

Rearing is done mainly by the male bird; he guards them from all predators and if necessary. he will attack by kicking with his very powerful legs. If necessary a male ostrich will try to create a diversion to get enemies away from the nest. He can gallop at great speed and will do so to avoid an attacker.

Feeding

As noted, the ostrich feeds on a wide variety of food–stuff. He takes grasses and plants, as well as berries. Certain insects and small reptiles will also be taken. However, the plant lucerne is the one best liked and suited to the ostrich and for this reason the domesticated bird is now fed on this

Figure 2.5 Ostriches on the Gallop

They will gallop away whenever there are serious enemies. If ostriches are in close confinement care must be taken to avoid them panicking or broken legs may occur from crashing into fences.

special plant. Great care must be taken not to leave metal or plastic objects around or the ostrich may injure itself by eating something which is much too large to digest or in the case of plastic cannot digest anyway.

Age for Breeding

The usual breeding age is four years , although domesticated stock may reach maturity a year or so earlier; therefore, it is wise for those who are commencing Ostrich farming to purchase stock between two and four years of age. They will then become reproductive almost immediately. As noted, very forward birds are in breeding condition at three years, but such birds do not usually give such good results as those which mature more slowly. The indications of breeding fitness are such that they cannot be mistaken. The cock becomes very red about the beaks and shins, he shows an enlargement under the tail, and his temper is not so reliable, in fact he often becomes very savage.

The indications shown by the hen that she has arrived at the breeding state are that she walks about with her head hanging down, by the manner in which she opens and shuts her beak when walking and by the rapidity with which she flaps her wings up and down.

Hatching

Incubation takes 6 weeks and the cock bird and one or more hens will take turn. Although the human assistance of chicks to hatch is never to be recommended, in the wild 'giving help' has been observed. The cock bird may get impatient and presumably because the process is taking too long he may break an egg by leaning on it with his chest and then remove the chick inside by shaking the membrane with his beak. He then eats the membrane and repeats the process.

Figure 2.6 The ostrich hiding from its enemies.
It does not bury its head in the sand as sometimes alleged. However, they will try all kind of tricks to avoid capture by those who hunt ostriches in the wild.

The Chicks

The chicks are able to move around and run within a short time of hatching. They depend on the parent for protection. In fact, the process is no different from the domestic fowl when the chicks are taken around picking up the food detected by the parents.

General Behaviour

As would be expected ostriches are nomads and therefore are wild and shy, no doubt due to the fact that over centuries they have been hunted and molested by man. Their eggs are taken for food and the carcases are also eaten and the skins used for a variety of uses. The egg shells are used for containing water and other purposes.

If attacked by someone wishing to capture the chicks the cock has been known to feign injury and lie on the ground until the hen and chicks escape. Only when the chicks are way ahead will he run in a different direction to distract the pursuers.

Domestication

The ostrich has been domesticated in Britain for hundreds of years. The first record appears to be at the time of Oliver Cromwell. Just after that time (1680) a Sir Thomas Browne of Norwich wrote to his son regarding two ostriches having just arrived from Tangiers. He also commented on earlier arrivals when he was a boy and, from information given to him by a Mr Clarke, of two ostriches in Cromwell's time.

London Zoo and other zoological gardens have kept them from Victorian times. As noted earlier, in Europe there was interest from around 1859.

3
SELECTION OF STOCK

GETTING GOOD STOCK

If stock is to be purchased from a breeder in this country or abroad it will be necessary to obtain proof of sound health. Some form of Veterinary Certificate will usually be essential and if purchased from abroad the regulations of the country in question will usually stipulate a quarantine period at an approved establishment. This should be contacted before making arrangements to determine whether new birds can be accepted and the cost of transportation and keep for the period involved which may be 3 months or even longer.

Criteria for Selection

In selecting birds for purchase and subsequently, when culling, it will be essential to ask:

Which birds are likely to be the most productive for breeding?

The ultimate choice must be based on future breeding potential and the selection criteria should be used at all times. These may be viewed in the light of **possible laying potential** and the **ability to reach specified weights within stated periods** (conversion from food to stated weight).

The indications on what are likely to be productive stock are :

1. Health and Stamina

Sound, healthy birds may be seen from watching them eat and behave. Those which are listless and droopy with little appetite are not likely to reach the required size or laying potential. Viewing of the parent stock is essential because any imperfections in these will show up at a later date in the offspring. If there are any defects, such as lameness or lack of size refuse to have any youngsters offered from such stock.

2. Feather Quality

Feathers should be of a high quality and strong.The essentials have been summarized as follows:

The feather, though strong and dense, must be firm in quality, not coarse and hairy. The plumes should be as dense and large as possible, the longer and broader the better. A good plume should measure twenty–two to twenty–five inches from tip to butt, whilst in breadth it should be from twelve to fifteen inches. Length and breadth, important though they be, are not everything; evenness and symmetrical proportion and finish must be considered.

The tips must be blunt and full, ported right through; the flue must be close and dense, and the barbules knit well up together. The stem or shaft should be strong, yet not harsh and stiff. If too stiff the natural curve of the plume is lost, and if it is weak it is too pliable and the plume falls instead of drooping gracefully.

There must be no gumminess, thinness, or stiffness about the flue, but it must be dense, firm in texture, and evenly fluffed. The feather as a whole must show a clear unbroken surface both in fibre and colour, and be quite free from bars.

Figure 3.1 Select strong birds with sound plumage for breeding stock

This is a South African Pair of ostriches

A SYSTEMATIC APPROACH

The newcomer may find great difficulty in selecting stock and guidance from others as suggested later in this chapter would be appropriate, but the ultimate decision must rest with the would–be farmer. He must be guided on what he can observe and what information he can obtain, usually from the person selling the stock.

A Questionnaire may be designed along the lines of the one given on the facing page, but it is also useful to have some idea of the answers which could be expected from ideal birds and following the adage: *you get the quality you pay for* , act on that basis.

You should compare prices in the market because these may fluctuate considerably. If stock is to be purchased from abroad make sure that you have a report from a reliable agent or, better still, visit the country involved.

There may be difficulty in getting direct answers to some of the questions because the breeder will be anxious to sell. However, usually a discussion will elicit many of the answers. Ideally birds of 5 or 6 years old should be sought because 3 year old may be unreliable. However, the ideal birds may be too expensive and it would be better to consider yearlings with a view to getting them accustomed to the new management before breeding with them. If so the questions will be directed at the parents' capabilities in the hope that the offspring will perform equally well or better.

Birds of 15 years of age should still be capable of breeding well so do not reject the offer of older birds out of hand. They will be steady and accustomed to hatching and rearing. The danger with 3–year old birds is that they will have difficulty in getting fertile eggs because the young cock tries too hard and the hen becomes alarmed and runs away from him.

QUESTIONNAIRE

Questions to be answered before purchase.

1. What are the prices and do these include some or all of the delivery costs.

2. What age are the birds.

3. How many years have they been breeding.

4. What number of nests do they have annually.

5. How many eggs do they lay per nest and in total.

6. How many times do they sit on the nests.

7. What is the percentage of success in hatching.

8. What is the percentage of successes in rearing.

9. Are the chicks strong and healthy.

10. Do the birds have any exceptional characteristics or known faults.

Figure 3.2 Assessing the Worth of possible Purchases.

As with all livestock it will take time for a new breeder to be able to select top class birds so advice should be sought from an experienced breeder. There are still zoos in existence and a bird–keeper may be able to advise on what to expect in a sound bird.

The purpose is to establish a strain which will grow quickly and surely, without weaknesses, and will continue to produce for many years. Once the correct combination has been achieved there should be reluctance to introduce untested, new blood. Any indiscriminate crossing may undo the work of many years and set back a breeding programme to an extent which might endanger future results in a damaging way. In fact, if in doubt, provided the stock is vigorous, it is better to inbreed, thus perpetuating the existing blood line. Only when there is a weakness in constitution, indicated by poor results, should new blood be necessary and then, preferably from the *same* strain, kept by another farmer.

Attention to the points mentioned here are most important, and birds selected on such lines will, if bred from an established strain, be calculated to produce chicks showing the same quality as their parents. The foundation stock should come from one strain. It is not wise to mix different families.

One hears much talk as to the value of different strains. This is due to the fact that those who hold those strains have, by careful selection and mating weeded out the birds which produced poor quality plumes, and established a race of birds which may reasonably be expected to yield nothing but the highest quality. This fixing of quality has been done by in–breeding, and nothing destroys the quality of a strain more quickly than the infusion of alien blood. Some breeders are afraid to in–breed. They need not be. In–breeding is the royal road to success when properly practised.

4
ESTABLISHING AN OSTRICH FARM

VITAL REQUIREMENTS

There are a number of essential requirements for successful ostrich farming. The size of the operation, based on what finance is available, will be a prime consideration. Forecasts and budgets will be necessary because it may be a few years before the operation will be profitable and have a positive cash flow to cover the needs. As noted earlier, in some cases it may be desirable to have some other form of farming, say, arable, which will give time for the new business to become established.

The existence of large sheds or barns will also be helpful and make the venture less costly to launch.

Admitting the possible variations in approach and the ways of ultimately achieving the business objectives the basic requirements will be as follows:

1. Fields for allowing grazing and for growing lucerne and other crops.
2. Sheds to house the birds.
3. Fenced enclosures for breeding and keeping the birds in manageable flocks.
4. Equipment for cutting lucerne and other vegetables.
5. Watering facilities and feeding hoppers.
6. Incubators and an incubator room or building.
7. Rearing rooms for stock of different ages, from day old upwards.
8. Store Rooms and related facilities, including an office for recording results.

GENERAL PRINCIPLES

These above aspects are now considered and are also touched upon in other parts of the book. As emphasized throughout this book, ostriches will not thrive well when exposed to extreme cold or very wet weather. Shelters are essential and , if necessary, they should be locked indoors; an open verandah may be ideal with an overhanging roof to stop rain or snow being blown in. This would also allow feeding troughs to be erected and chopped lucerne, clover, mangolds and other food can be given daily making sure to clear away the old food when the new is given. In effect, this is an extension of the Barn/ Aviary systems used for domestic poultry, although obviously on a much larger scale or fewer birds.

Fences should be at least 5 feet tall because ostriches can leap very high. Moreover, there should be emergency exits in case the cock bird gets aggressive. It is also recommended that there are no sharp corners where ostriches can 'pile up' when there is a stampede from being badly frightened. Fortunately this should not occur very frequently, but if birds are on the wild side that danger is possible.

The safety of the keepers must also be kept in mind when designing or building enclosures. The male ostrich in breeding condition becomes a strutting, difficult individual and if he decides to become aggressive, then move out of his way. If he starts to kick it might be safer to lie down and hope he goes away. Sometimes he will roll on the unfortunate individual who will be severely bruised. The safest way is to keep out of the enclosure in the breeding season and only use keepers that the cock knows and trusts. A shepherd's crook is useful because if the neck can be caught the ostrich can be controlled. With care and attention there should be little danger to the experienced stock person.

Fields Required

A poultry farm could well be adapted for ostriches, but the two types should not be run together and there should be no question of the ostriches being exposed to diseases which have been left behind.

Possibly an arable or dairy farm would be the best choice, especially if barns and other outbuildings are available for adaption. The need for suitable land to grow lucerne, mangolds, rape, barley and wheat is also desirable.

The fields may be divided into smaller enclosures (known as 'camps' in the literature on ostrich farming) for lucerne to be grown and on which birds may be run. Alternatively, the lucerne may be harvested by cutting on a regular basis and then, after being shredded, fed to the ostriches which are kept in separate enclosures. If free range farming is to be practised it will be essential to rotate the usage of fields (enclosures) so that whilst some are are being used, others are being 'rested'.

It has been stated on good authority that: *if it is the wish of the farmer to conduct operations on a large scale he should secure land where irrigation developments are possible, and where lucerne will grow in profusion, because without lucerne it is practically impossible to be successful. In Ostrich rearing rape, desert melons, mangolds and American aloes are all necessary growths for the Ostrich farmer.*

The farmer in a climate harsher than that experienced in South Africa must modify his plans to what is achievable. Such vegetables as desert melons are not likely to grow very successfully in Britain!

The fact that lucerne is the ideal crop is acknowledged, but other, similar plants may be substituted in Britain, because growing clover is no problem.

Sheds and other Accommodation

Writing of experience in South Africa an expert on ostrich farming had this to state:

> **Those farmers who value their stock erect huts or shelters in their camps; it is not absolutely necessary, but better results are attained when huts are provided. These huts, which are made of reeds and rushes, are about twelve or fourteen feet deep from front to back, ten or twelve feet wide, and nine or ten feet high, they are built in apex form and help the birds considerably.**
>
> **At first the birds are rather shy of the huts, but their shyness is easily overcome by feeding inside. When they have become accustomed to the hut, they will often make use of its sheltering cover, and will later make their nest inside. These huts should be well fastened to the ground to prevent them from being lifted by the storms. When the cock begins to drive the hen out, place an egg inside the hut, the birds will soon get used to it, and will make their nest on the hut floor. Should they lay outside in the camp they may be induced to use the hut by three or four eggs being placed near the front and then removed inside a day or so later.**

In a situation where there are predators, thieves and inclement weather more substantial dwellings will be necessary. A large shed of brick or wood would be vital with a ceiling height of not less than two metres and preferably insulated with some internal board, thus keeping the temperature reasonable even in a wintry, cold spell.

Opposite ::::::::::::::::::::::>>>>>>>>>>>>>>>>

Figure 4.1 A pair of Ostriches on a South African farm. The male is the larger, mainly black bird. Although a number of hens may be run with a cock a one–to–one ratio is considered ideal by some.

Note the sheds in the background for housing and the very superior fences. Because of cost, wire may be used rather than rods as shown.

See caption opposite

Covered Shelter is Essential

In climates where there is much rain, snow and frost a covered shelter will be advisable. Like many other birds which originate from warmer climates, although quite hardy, they cannot stand dampness and severe cold unless given dry shelter.

The size of the shed should allow sufficient room for all the birds to be housed without overcrowding; at least two square metres per grown bird should be the allowance. This would certainly be the case for winter when birds have to be kept indoors for days at a time. Much depends on circum-stances so birds let out daily can manage with less indoor cover, but there must still be room to sit and relax. However, if at all possible the birds should be let out each day, but not in very wet, cold weather because they may not dry out very well and breathing problems would result. Earlier in this chapter it was noted that the **Barn system**, with a wire front may be appropriate, which gives plenty of fresh air and some exercise, as well as allowing easy feeding.

In fact ostrich accommodation may be thought of in terms of **many small units** to house, say, a pair, or **on a large scale , with a very large building**, with partitions and separate enclosures running off from each apartment. A corridor down the middle of the barn allowing a vehicle to be pushed along, could also be part of the arrangement.

Opposite ::::::::::::::::::::::**>>>>>>>>>>>>>**

Figure 4.2 Ostriches in adjacent pens

Note the house in the background with windows for ventilation in the summer. Also the entrance door for access. The fencing is topped with chain link fencing to a height of about 5 ft and the bottom is boarded with stout boards to give protection. It should be noted that a *double* fence (with a gap between) is regarded by many as essential to avoid conflict, but this depends on the stock and how much can be spent.

See caption opposite

ENCLOSURES

If birds are to be managed properly they should be kept in manageable size flocks. Growing stock may be in relatively large numbers, but a breeding pen would be a few hens to a male. Because of predators, birds must be locked away each evening. There is also the need to train them to become accustomed to a particular house so that they will return to it to rest each evening.

Experience in South Africa indicates there are certain sizes and other requirements. These would have to be modified in the light of what is available, but it should be appreciated that overcrowding will not be conducive to profitable farming. It may be a short term expedient, but long term it will also be folly because once the ground becomes muddy or barren the birds will not thrive.

A properly fitted enclosure is most essential to success, therefore great attention should be paid to the various aspects.

Fences should be erected and these should be at least five feet apart, and the space between should be planted with bushes as wind breakers*.

Plain wire should be used for the fences, the top strand should be at least five feet high, and the lower twenty or twenty-two inches, with four intermediate strands. The double fence is necessary to prevent fighting amongst the birds. The fences should be strongly and firmly fixed so as to avoid accidents. Double fences such as here described are undoubtedly the most efficient, but if the initial expense is too great, a simple yet effective form of fence can be made by erecting a single wire about the height of an Ostrich's breast three feet from the fence. Deer wire or similar may also be

***In South Africa the recommendation is prickly pear and American aloes, but these would only be appropriate in a warm climate. Any non-toxic hedge should suffice.**

used, but care must be exercised to ensure that an ostrich is not given a situation where he pushes his head into a wire square and then cannot remove it. Remember ostriches do not fly although they can leap a tremendous distance.

Views on Requirements

A cross view of requirments is useful when deciding what should be done as regards accommodation, space and fencing. Generally the more space the better, but the cost of managing set against the dangers of overcrowding must be balanced. The following notes are relevant:

1. The space required would vary according to the age of the birds. Growers may be kept in relatively large numbers whereas fully grown stock would require a field for an enclosure, generally at a stocking rate of around 10 per acre, although this figure may be exceeded up to 20 birds per acre in very favourable conditions. On the large farms of South Africa many acres might be used to graze the ostriches; camps of 30/40 acres are not unusual for a breeding pen of a cock and, say, two hens.
On a large farm it was not unusual to think in terms of around 500 birds on 200 acres, but this had to be top quality land growing lucerne under irrigation. and not the poorer quality scrub land on which ostriches will thrive, but not in large numbers. The food intake is enormous; on one farm the ostriches (550) would eat 40 tons of hay in 50 days of winter which would be replaced with the lucerne as it began to grow.

2. In South Africa it has long been recognized that ostriches must be reared and grazed on alkali soil which contains minerals. Where this type of soil was not available an alternative had to be found, ***usually phosphate of lime of bones, sulphur and salt must be given to supplement the food if not available naturally.*** (this is a summary of a report on the subject). Fortunately modern food technology is able to supply any special requirements as shown by the specially formulated foods for each main type of poultry food such as that for layers, turkeys, broilers or pheasants.

Size of Enclosure

Usually an area of not less than half an acre would be the recommended minimum for keeping even one ostrich. The RSPCA* gives one quarter of an acre open paddock as a minimum size and 15 per acre as the maximum stocking density, but stresses these are standards which should be bettered if possible.

An ostrich farmer suggests that a breeding pen for a cock and two hens should be about 100 metres square, and should consist entirely of lucerne, or half lucerne and half rough and bushes or arable. If the proper attention is paid to the birds the latter form of may be reckoned to give the best results, because the supply of green food in the way of chopped lucerne and green rape, lucerne hay**, is limited to what the owner or his attendants give the birds, but much depends on the attention given.

Some breeders have found that running the ostriches on grass land, cut short and allowed to grow new grass, is more acceptable than allowing the birds to run in the lucerne field. Although the feed has to be given daily it means that the main crop is not spoilt by the birds fouling the pasture. In turn it means that the crop will continue to be harvested for a number of years. Lucerne may be cropped for four or five years in the appropriate conditions.

SUITABILITY OF SOIL

For free range to be successful, attention must be paid to the type and condition of the soil. A well drained, light loam is ideal so that mud is kept to a minimum; if necessary

---

******Welfare standards, etc*, **ibid.**

**** In warmer climates prickly pear, aloe and other cheap crops are also used. There is a need to experiment with suitable foods for winter feed.**

small pebbles or gravel can be placed near access doors for the birds and the main door so that mud is not carried indoors and possibly on to the eggs.

Avoiding the "Burnt Grass Effect"

Brown patches appearing on free range is known as the "Burnt Grass Effect". It means that the pasture is being abused and is no longer able to function properly and supply food.

The **Burnt Grass effect** can be avoided by putting birds on new land at regular intervals with sufficient time to allow new grass to grow. There is a conflict; **low** stocking will save wear on grass, but will not provide adequate use of the land, building and equipment.

Always there is a tendency for birds to stay within easy reach of the house where food and water are available. Thus with the large house the existing grass will quickly disappear and the question is what next? Movement of the stock is the ideal, but cannot always be done very easily. The provision of grass clippings from lawns, paddocks, etc., may provide a solution and the dumping of leaves and similar foraging material is desirable, provided always that the litter is edible and no danger to health.

Avoid Mud and 'Water Holes'

In a wet climate ostriches may churn up a field very quickly and cause puddles in which they may roll. This practice is detrimental to the birds generally and may cause considerable damage to the feathers. In these circumstances it will be better to have a barn in which birds can be kept during the wet, cold months. Hay or shavings can be supplied as bedding, thus making the quarters quite comfortable. A dust bath of dry sand, mixed with ash and sulphur powder will allow the birds to 'bathe' and dust themselves to eliminate parasites.

Equipment for cutting food

The standard type of cutting machine turned by hand or engine will be adequate for cutting lucerne, mangolds and other crops. Daily preparation is to be recommended. For chicks the cuttings should be short and fine.

Figure 4.3 A Typical cutting machine
Many variations may be found which perform similar tasks.

Watering and feeding facilities

A regular supply of fresh water is vital and water containers should be provided. Unfortunately, many of the hoppers and drinking fountains for poultry are too small for ostriches. Accordingly, it will be necessary to provide hoppers and other utensils used for cattle or pigs.

Water Tub (Galvanized)

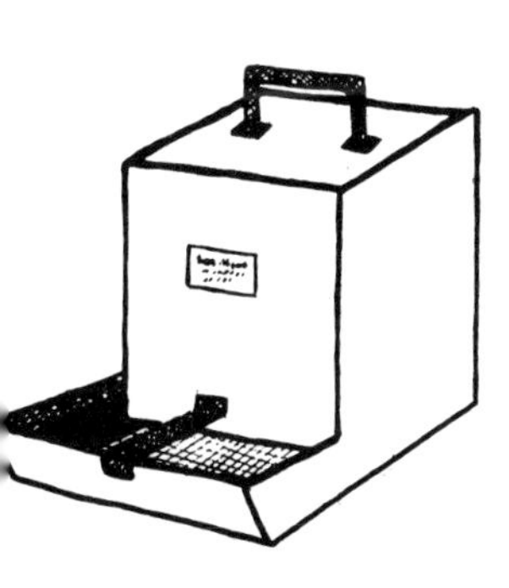

Water Container

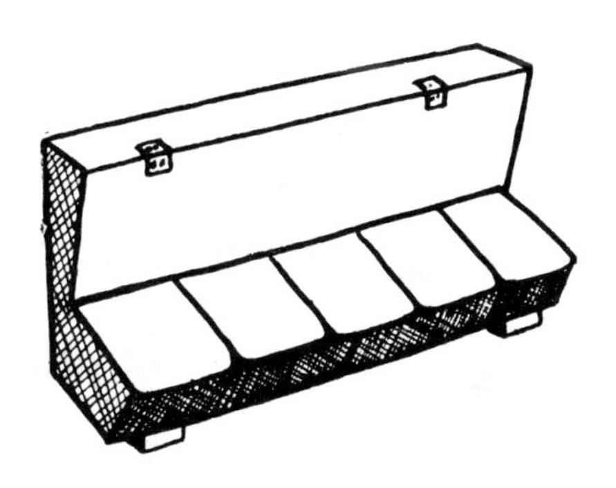

Figure 4.4 Typical utensils which may be used for ostriches' food and water.

It will be necessary to experiment and remember that food should be cleared daily and water should be fresh.

INCUBATOR(S) AND SUITABLE ROOM

The selection of a suitable incubator is an essential requirement for ostrich farming. This may be a standard type, used for hen eggs, or a **special Ratite incubator** which allows automatic turning. Because of the large size of ostrich eggs the normal incubator cannot cope with the vital turning which must be done by hand.

The principles for building an incubation room are well established. It should be of the type that avoids fluctuations in temperature and preferably have a concrete floor for washing and disinfecting. Generally a brick building, well insulated and without windows, would be the ideal.

There should be sufficient space for keeping the eggs whilst awaiting loading into the incubator. However, the best temperature for storing, cleaning and other pre–incubation tasks may be better done in a separate adjoining room.

Rearing rooms for chicks

Chicks are best reared indoors for the first few months, particularly in inclement weather. Accordingly, provision should be made to house the chicks at different ages. There should be no mixing of different generations because this leads to all kinds of problems from bullying to the spread of disease.

Store rooms for food and an office

Provision of store rooms for food will be vital. This will enable it to be kept away from vermin and at the correct temperature.

The office may be adjoining so that food consumption can be recorded, along with other vital facts such as production of eggs and food conversion.

If a large business then a separate office for accounting, marketing and administration will be necessary.

5

FEEDING OSTRICHES

BASIC PRINCIPLES

The principles of feeding poultry are well established, but with the ostrich there are many aspects which are dis-similar to the normal fowl so we cannot simply feed poultry pellets and expect maximum results. As noted earlier, in many ways the ostrich is part animal and apparently thrives best on a diet of lucerne and vegetation with supplementary protein, supplied in captivity in the form of barley meal or other corn. It is against this background that a diet must be formulated.

Early Methods

The farmers of South Africa established that lucerne and mangolds, supplemented when appropriate was the best approach, viz:

> **In addition to their green food the birds should have mealies (maize) or barley meal twice a day, not more than one pound to each bird at each time of feeding. It sometimes happens that birds are backward in coming into breeding condition. When this is so a few feeds of recommended barley, and mangolds are of much service in bringing them up to concert pitch. From the time when the hens commence laying the grain should be stopped, otherwise the bend will become too fat and will not lay. Further, the cock will become so gross and rampant that he will worry the hens, chase them off the nest and generally upset things, so that the majority of the eggs will be unfertile, and the chicks which do hatch will be weak and sickly, whilst instead of producing two or three nests in the season the hens will only go to nest once.**

One well-known and successful farmer turns his breeding birds out into the fields on January 1st*. There they get plenty of exercise, plenty of grit, complete change, and nothing but the natural food available which brings them into pre-laying condition by March 31st. When brought into camp (enclosure) each bird is given half-a-pound of mealies (maize) twice a day, and they find what green food they like from the lucerne, grass, and bushes. When they have been in a month they usually commence breeding, with the result that the eggs are very fertile and the chicks strong and healthy.

EXPERIENCES FROM POULTRY FARMING

Because of the vast experience available in the poultry industry it is possible to use the foodstuffs developed in their original form or modify them to suit the larger bird. Readily available are:

1.Layers' Pellets

These contain the necessary amino acids within the food as well as the required levels of calcium to achieve good quality shells. They can be obtained for 'free range' layers which are better than the battery-type (intensive) pellets.

An alternative is to use Turkey Layers' Pellets because these are for larger birds.

2. Table Poultry Pellets (Broilers')

These are similar to layers' pellets , but mixed to give the appropriate level of growth. There are no coccidiostats or anti blackhead drugs in the pellets, but other drugs may be present.

3. Chick Crumbs

These are available for feeding young chicks. A formula used for these is given below. It will be appreciated that mixing foods is a very skilled task and is best left to the experts. Turkey starter crumbs may give better results.

*** The exact date will depend on the climate and may have to be delayed slightly in the UK.**

FORMULA FOR CHICK CRUMBS

A formula used by a feeding stuffs manufacturer is shown below:

GOLD START CRUMBS ACS

A complete animal feedstuff for feeding either *ad lib* or restricted to chicks up to 8 weeks of age:
OIL 4.0% PROTEIN 18.0% FIBRE 4.0% ASH 6.8% M.E. 11.4 Mj/KG

Vitamin A (iu.kg) 9,000
Vitamin D3 (iu/kg) 1,800
Vitamin E-alpha-tocopherol (iu/kg) 20
Sodium Selenite-Selenium (mg/kg) 0.3
Sodium Molybdate-Molybdenum(mg/kg) 2
Cupric Sulphate -Copper (mg/kg) 20

This product is a medicated animal feedstuff. At the time of manufacture the following was added:

ANTI-COCCIDIAL SUPPLEMENT; AVATEC PREMIX (PO0031.4011) 700g/tonne to provide 105 mg/kg LASALOCID SODIUM as an aid in the prevention of coccidiosis.

It will be seen that all essential proteins, minerals and vitamins are included. There is also a warning **NOT** to feed this food after 8 weeks of age. An important principle of feeding is that the foodstuff should be appropriate to the type and age of birds being fed. There is little point in feeding a very high protein to growers intended for laying because too early maturity can result in starting laying with small eggs.

Similarly once hens have reached physical maturity they should not require as much protein to maintain the body (although still required for laying) and, therefore, this can be reduced with a saving in costs.

Note: Before using any foodstuff mixed for ostrich chicks check with the manufacturer to ensure suitability. Skilled nutritionists are willing to advise with any problems.

Chicks Unusual Eating Habits

In the process of rearing with the ostrich hen it will be found that the chicks eat the solid excrement of the older birds. This may be nature's way of providing easily digested food (Compare **pigeon milk**), or this may be a process of building immunity from disease or both.

Possibly it is for that reason that some farmers prefer to rear the chicks with the hen, but there is no proof of great benefit from this approach. In fact, a hen may 'run the birds into the ground' many being lost. It is vital they have exercise, but not excessive in the early weeks.

Alternatively, if a hen is used to hatch eggs and then the chicks are reared artificially it will be necessary to take them from the mother at an early age, preferably within a few days or they may become wild when they have a very large paddock for exercise.

In South Africa it was found that the young should be brought back to the homestead at the end of three days and from then on the chicks would be fed by a native boy who would be responsible for their welfare. This allowed the chicks to become domesticated and in turn allowed them to be part of the ostrich farm environment. Left to themselves, with little contact with humans they would revert to the wild.

This process of domestication and its consequences, including its impact on the wild creature's future behaviour has now been recognized by scientists and is called '**imprinting**'. At the extreme the birds or animals concerned regard the humans with which they have had contact as their parents. This has occurred with geese, lambs, dogs and other creatures. In fact, this is one of the problems facing those who try to improve conservation by breeding in captivity and releasing into the wild. The once wild creatures become domesticated and can no longer cope with the problems and enemies of the external environment.

Figure 5.1 Lucerne

The mainstay of the diet of the Ostrich, but requires suitable soil and climate. Clover may be more suitable in a very wet climate.

Food Ingredients

The grain and other ingredients must comply with the standards laid down for poultry. They include soya, bran, wheat, lucerne , seaweed meal , and grass meal all grown in a natural way. Vegetable oil and fish meal , as well as certain approved vitamins and minerals, are also included. Food must also be sterilized so the feeding of ground bones as previously should not be attempted unless they have been cooked in a pressure cooker or other, similar process.

FEEDING OSTRICHES

As noted,the ostriches feed on a wide variety of food–stuff. They take grasses and plants, as well as berries. Cer–tain insects and small reptiles will also be taken. However, the plant **lucerne** is the one best liked and suited to the ostrich and for this reason the domesticated bird is fed on this special plant. In climates where there is ample rainfall (eg, Britain) a good quality clover may be substituted.

Special pelleted foods are now available for feeding adult birds, but lucerne is the ideal staple food which is supplemented by pellets, wheat, maize and barley and vari–ous chopped root crops.

This food should be given in adequate quantities to maintain body weight and produce eggs. A guide to the amount is as follows :

1. Pellets or similar food...... 45g per 11k of weight

Special rations are available in the UK (**Special Diet Services, Witham, Essex**) or in the USA (**ZuPreem**). These consist of various ingredients and vitamins as well as calcium. They follow very closely the recipes used for poultry. The main difference lies in the level of protein included, especially for rearing birds. We believe that with sound management and a wide variety of foods the ostriches will thrive very well on poultry foodstuff with lucerne, mangolds and similar roots and greens.

The foodstuff recommended has percentage levels of around: Protein 14%, calcium 2.5%, phosphore 1.25% and vitamins A, E and D3.

The quantity of food in the form of pellets, maize and other grain is around 1lb. per laying bird, but this guide must be used with caution because it depends on other foods being given and the number of eggs being produced.

2. Lucerne or alfalfa as it is also known.

This is a clover-like plant which is said to derive its name from Lucerne in Switzerland, although not all agree with this origin. Indeed, it has been known from ancient times, being mentioned by Virgil and other very early writers. It is said to be rich in albumen and is very nutritious.

The plant is termed 'fabaceous with trifoliolate leaves and purple flowers resembling a clover flower with loose heads'. It is also known as a leguminous plant, referring to the bean-like seeds.

The reason for its use and development as a food for animals and ostriches in countries where rainfall is very sparse is because of its ability to withstand drought, the roots developing to a great depth and continuing to grow in adverse weather conditions.

The soil must be deep loam so the roots can grow well into the ground. Clay should be avoided and lime is essen– tial. If water in the form of rain is excessive and this remains on the surface lucerne will not thrive and a good strain of clover should be used.

In the first year the crop should be cut and used as chopped fodder. This allows the roots to develop which may push down many feet. After that the ostriches may be al– lowed to graze, although as note earlier, some farmers prefer to cut and feed in a separate enclosure.

The crop may be taken three or possibly more times per year and whilst it can be made into hay this is not satisfactory for ostriches because it becomes hard and brittle. A solution may be to wet the hay or to produce silage from it. Other types of grass hay or straw may be more acceptable.

Figure 5.2 Roots of Lucerne
Showing great depth achieved (4.5 years' old)

3. Greens and soaked corn, oats and barley
Any normal green stuff will be taken and corn, etc may be soaked or given whole or may be ground into a coarse flour.

4. Grit of various types
Grit is of two kinds:
(a) Flint for grinding the food in the gizzard;
(b) Soluble grit for calcium required as part of the diet and for making the egg shells.

Both must be available. The grit for calcium may be limestone, oyster shells and cockle shells, suitably ground into small pieces.

It should be kept under cover in suitable containers.

Note:
The aim should be to give **variety and a balanced diet**; the above is a guide only and may be varied to suit circumstances and conditions.

Ostriches, like many other domesticated birds, are creatures of habit. Make sure they are given a varied diet so they become accustomed to eating all the main foods they are likely to be given. Otherwise, when a new food is introduced in adult life they may refuse to take it.

Note: For detailed descriptions of the various foods readers are referred to *Practical Poultry Keeping* , J Batty.

Figure 5.3

6

INCUBATION

HATCHING THE EGGS

There is nothing more exciting or worthwhile in poultry keeping that the creation of new life from the eggs which have been laid by the selected stock. How the process should be carried out depends very much on the size of the operation.

NATURAL INCUBATION

There are some who follow the old-fashioned methods and let the birds do the hatching, others more progressive let the birds sit for the first half or two-thirds of the incubatory period, and then finish off in an incubator; some use incubators from the start to finish.

When the birds begin to lay see that a nest is well made for them because a well-made nest means that the eggs are not so likely to get cracked or broken.

The nest should be made nice and soft with plenty of sand, but not too much, under the eggs, and all stones and rough material should be carefully removed. It is wise to bank the nest which protects the eggs from being flooded in case of heavy rain, and prevents them rolling away from the nest. A well-made nest conduces greatly to a successful hatching.

Making the Nest

How to make a nest has been described by an ostrich farmer in the following terms:

> **...a proper place is prepared for the nest, after three or four eggs have been laid, by digging a hole 6ft wide by 2ft deep beside the original nest, and filling it with gravel, to secure drainage in the event of heavy rain occurring while the birds are sitting. After the birds become familiar with the alterations the birds are moved on to the place prepared for them.**

It goes without saying that there must be adequate protection against predators and, if possible, the nest should be in some form of shelter and a breeding pair of birds should be encouraged to go inside to prepare a nest, but this is not always achieved so an outside nest, as described, will be essential.

The hen ostrich is generally quite amenable whilst the laying is going on, but can be fierce when hatching commences. The cock may turn nasty and charge at any time when in season. Usually the breeding period starts about May and continues until September.

Once the hatching starts keep away from the hen, although an inspection is advisable at the end of the hatch. Generally a quiet visit at night time, two in attendance and a strong light, will allow the hen to be raised slightly and the results observed. The chicks will not require any attention, food or water for the first two days.

If the chicks are to be reared artificially then they should be moved and place in a heated rearer, possibly under infra-red lamps. However, should they be left with the mother ostrich a suitable place for rearing should be found so that the chicks are rested for the first few days and then given exercise once they are quite strong. Moving them means an earlier start to the laying, but imposes a further burden with rearing.

The eggs should lie flat, and not be allowed to get on top of each other. An ostrich hen will cover from fifteen to twenty eggs. Much depends on the size of the eggs, also the size of the hen. Safety lies in having one too few, rather than one too many. As noted earlier, a communal nest can be very wasteful and should be discouraged for only the centre eggs hatch.

In the records put down all the relevant details of the eggs. The date sat, number in nest, cock responsible and hen and during the hatch keep a note of any difficulties, such as the hen not being steady on the nest or the cock being a nuisance. After the hatching record the number of chicks and the success rate. If below 75% success there will be something wrong with the food or the birds may be the wrong age. Sometimes the first eggs in the season are not fertile because of excess cold or the cock not yet up to the required level of fitness.

Removing the Eggs

When the hen starts laying, it is wise to take the eggs away day by day leaving an old egg in the nest to keep the hen quiet. When this is done there is no fear of damage being done to the eggs by sun or frost, or their being destroyed by predators, who, if given the chance, will destroy many a nest before the hens start incubating. When the eggs are taken away, they should be marked so as to know which hen has laid them, and they should be kept in a locked room on fine sand, sawdust, of some other soft material; a special wooden frame or box can be made. This will prevent them from rolling about and being cracked or chipped. Care must also be used in handling the eggs, as accidents happen very easily. The eggs should be stored at a relatively cool temperature, but not frozen.

INCUBATION IN CAPTIVITY

As noted, there are different ways of incubating the eggs laid by the ostrich hens:

1. The ostrich itself

This method means the output from each hen will be restricted and therefore is not to be recommended. It may also be wasteful and the broody hen may get her plumage damaged whilst sitting.

2. An Incubator

(a) Adapted from a normal machine with larger spaces, or
(b) A Ratite Incubator specially developed for hatching the eggs from ostriches and similar eggs.

The advantage of the special incubator is its ability to turn the eggs automatically and to be able to cope with such large eggs. Buckeye manufacture these machines and therefore will advise on their use.

3. Large broody hens

The use of such birds as Plymouth Rocks, Rhode Island Reds or Barnevelders. The problem is that a hen can cover very few eggs and there would be difficulty turning them. No matter how large the hen selected there is bound to be difficulty. She will be perched on top of these giant eggs, which in itself will require great skill.

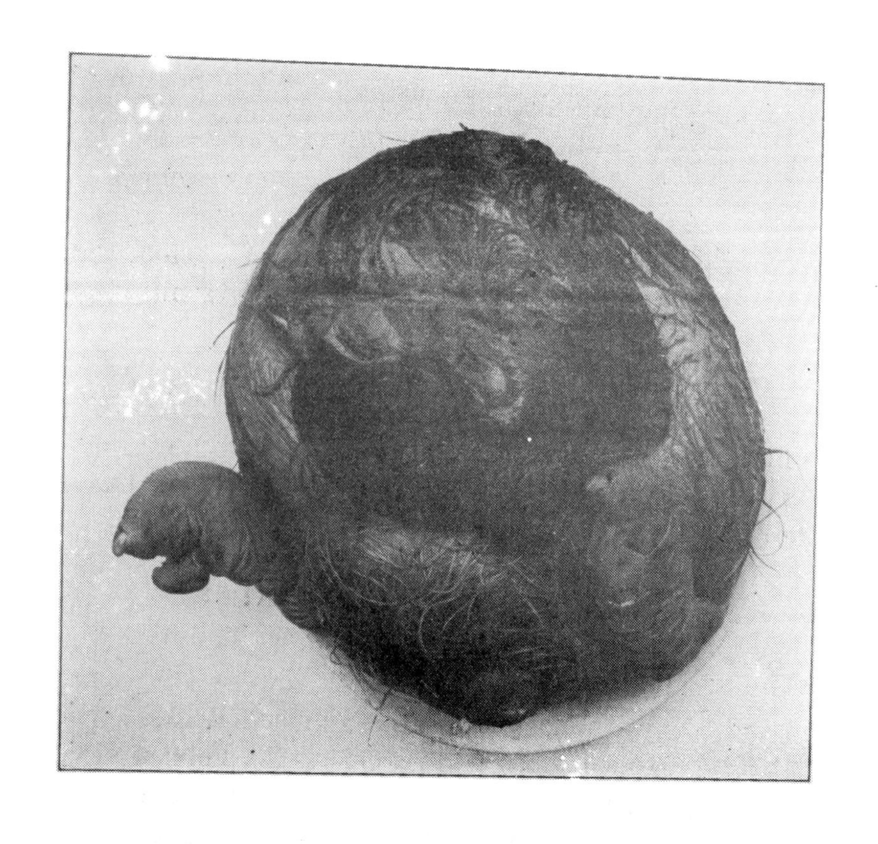

Figure 6.1 Embryo at 40 days
At this age the chick is about to try to emerge from the shell.

The Standard Incubator

Turning

The normal hen incubator will not be able to cope with turning the large eggs and therefore they should be turned by hand a number of times. **The optimum number of times is reckoned to be in the region of 4 to 6 per day**. This operation is critical and without it the yolk may stick to the shell and affect the growth of the embryo.

Advantage of Incubator

All incubators free the hen from the incubation process and therefore avoid the spoiling or soiling of feathers when natural incubation is employed. The loss of egg production has already been noted.

Incubators can be managed more effectively and a larger number of eggs can be dealt with than using hens. Also with ostrich eggs there is the great size to cope with and turning and handling is difficult by hand or by domesticated fowl.

Fresh Eggs Essential

Eggs placed in an incubator should be recently laid ; certainly not more than 7 days old. They should be collected each day and marked with the date and a code for showing the source of the egg , ie, the hen responsible. This should allow records to be compiled to show the output from each hen and the fertility achieved. Ostrich eggs are very valuable so a proper understanding of the results is vital because this will be the basis of future managerial action.

Checking the Embryo (Candling)

Regular candling of the eggs is also essential using a

very strong light to check on the development of the embryo. A start should be made at about 10 days , although some leave them until 21 days so the development cannot be mistaken.

Without proper attention or because the germ in the egg was weak anyway (due to wrong feeding or unfit stock) the embryo may die and this has to be detected as soon as possible. Generally a blurred image will show up when the candling is done-- instead of a dark, distinct form when a live embryo is present.

Any peculiar smell should be investigated because rotten eggs can play havoc with results, especially if an egg explodes. Fresh eggs not contaminated in any way by dirt or faeces do not usually turn bad so the principle to follow is obvious : only use newly laid, clean eggs. Whether to wash in a special disinfectant is a debatable issue, but if there is danger of bacteria then the washing should be tackled using only a solution approved for this purpose.

Weight Losses

Experienced aviculturists have developed tables for showing the moisture content of the egg at different stages and this allows the correct level of humidity to be established, simply by weighing the eggs at regular intervals, say, every two days. The results are then recorded.

This is a relatively new technique and is very useful when limited numbers are being hatched and the incubation operation is not capable of being controlled accurately, but whether it can be justified for every hatch will have to be decided by the farmer. Usually, from experience, the incubator operator can see the rate of evaporation by watching the air space in each egg and if too small or too large then take steps to correct the temperature, ventilation or humidity.

RUNNING THE INCUBATOR

As regards temperature and humidity the instructions on the incubator should be followed. Generally, eggs should be started at 99^0 F (37.2 C) and let it rise to 100^0F (37.7C) with reasonable humidity, but increasing at the 38th day. The precise figures will depend on the type of machine being used.

Practical Guidance

Guidance from a practical source, experienced in ostrich farming is reproduced:

General Guidance

The period of incubation is forty two days, but we need not be anxious if the eggs do not always hatch on the forty-second day; they sometimes go one, two and three days over, and we have heard of them hatching on the forty-ninth day.

A very successful Ostrich farmer, who used an incubator says he has done so with the best results. He gives the following advice as the the best method to pursue:-

"The fresher the eggs the better the results attending incubation. Start your incubator at ninety-nine degress, and keep it so for a couple of days, and then let it go up to one hundred degrees, your chicks should then hatch on the forty-first day. You must from the thirty-eighth day carefully watch the water tray, as the eggs just before hatching seem to draw up a lot of water. I have noticed if there is not sufficent mositure that the shells of the eggs get very hard, and this is not conducive to sucessful hatching.

Turning

From the time they are put in the incubator the eggs should be turned once each day* until the fortieth day; some say they should not be turned for the first two days, why we cannot understnad. The hen turns them in the nest so that we only follow nature by doing the same when they are in the incubator.

***As noted earlier, three or four times per day is advised.**

Candling

When the eggs have been in the incubator for three weeks they may be tested as to ferility. To test successfully cover the head and shoulders with a dark cloth, take the egg, hold it in front of the face, pulling the cloth well up to it and shutting out the light from the inside of the cloth, turn the face to the sun and look at the egg; if it is fertile it will show a dark spot on one side.* The egg should be held with the end containing the air space uppermost. If the egg is clear it should be removed as it is useless to keep the incubator filled with unfertile eggs.

At this period no doubt may be entertained as to the testing as, if the dark spot does not show then, it never will. Some breeders test at an earlier date than that we mention, as early as the fourteenth day, but one cannot be certain at that date, and it is as well to wait until one can be certain that the test is effective. If by any chance an egg should go rotten the fact will soon be known by the distinctly objectionable odour that will be manifested when the incubator is opened. The senses of sight and smell will quickly enable the attendant to detect the offending egg, which should at once be removed, for should it happen to burst in the incubator the chances are that the whole hatching would be spoilt. We might mention here that such a catastrophe is not likely to happen if none but fresh eggs are placed in the incubator.

The eggs should be cooled each day according to the instructions sent with each machine.++ Should an egg feel cold to touch when being turned at any time after the testing at three weeks then you may be pretty confident it will not hatch. If the eggs have only been in the incubator part of the incubation period it will be wise to test any: doubtful egg again to make certain as to its fertile or otherwise, as I sometimes happens that an egg is cooled by being on the outside of the nest, or may have been kicked on one side by one of the birds and then rolled back into

---

*** These notes were written in South Africa long ago and using the sun can be appropriate for testing eggs, but a very strong light situated where eggs and/ or trays can be placed will be more certain and acceptable.**

++ Not all agree with daily cooling of the eggs and it now seems certain that it is an unnecessary operation. The objective was to simulate the broody hen who leaves the nest every day and the eggs cool down. Consult the incubator instructions from the manufacturer.

the nest.

Cleanliness

One thing to be remembered in regard to successful artificial incubation is **the necessity for absolute cleanliness**. Therefore the incubating room and the machine also should be thoroughly cleansed before operations commence.

At the commencement of the season the machine should, after being cleansed, be given a trial run for two or three days; for succeeding hatchings the testing or trial run is not required, but the same necessity for thorough cleaning exists just the same.

An even temperature and free ventilation must prevail throughout the incubatory period, both in the house and the machine. This is an important point, and: one which should not be neglected.

An expert in Ostrich breeding says :

" If the eggs are examined a few days previous to hatching it will be noticed that the air space gets larger, the chick settling down in the egg until it only occupies about two thirds of the space in the shell. It then rises up again, until it almost, and in some instances quite fills the the whole space. At this stage it is well to mark the eggs at the air space end and if these eggs do not break within twelve hours it is advisable to open them.

Testing should be done morning and evening at the hatching time so that any chick not able to break himself out should be helped*. Make an opening and hold the egg to the light, a slight discolouration of the inner covering should be seen; this will indicate the position of the head, and enable the attendant to aid the chick, which he can do by breaking the egg all round, leaving the chick to kick himself free of the shell, or helping him along from time to time if he is not strong enough to manage for himself."

*** Many would disagree and would very rarely assist the hatching because if not done at the precise moment when the yolk has absorbed and the blood circulatory system is intact there is danger of bleeding and death. They consider that more chicks are killed than are saved by interference, as it often happens that from some cause or other an egg is longer in hatching, and any anxiety or impatience on the part of the attendant is fatal. Still it must be recorded that whilst some regularly assist their chicks into the world, others do not, and both are successful provided the timing is correct when assistance is given.**

Hatching

Although some incubators will hatch the eggs many systems require a separate hatcher which allows heat and humidity to be exactly correct for the hatching. For the first 24 hours the chicks should be kept in the hatcher and then moved to a rearing unit.

Where there is no separate hatcher the 24 hour rest period for drying is still essential--in the incubator drawer.

CHOICE OF INCUBATOR

The choice of incubator will depend on the size of op-eration and the recources available. A normal forced air incubator, modified to take the large eggs will probably be adequate for those who keep a few ostriches and wish to hatch occasionally. On the other hand, if ostrich farming is to be practised, it is false economy to make do with second best.

The best known of the special incubators are those made by Buckeye. They may be obtained in:

1. Free-standing and hold 60 or 120 eggs and may serve as an incubator or hatcher or both.

2. Built-in for hatching large numbers of eggs. These start at 216 egg size and go up to over 2,500 eggs.

A separate hatcher is recommended because this al-lows the exact conditions to be obtained for maximum hatch-ability.

Special standard trays and trolleys facilitate the tranfer and removal of the eggs to the incubator or hatcher.

The incubators may be obtained to allow for single hatching from start to finish (regarded as the best system) or may allow for eggs to be added, say each week, thus having chick embryos of different ages in the same machine. This method is the most economic when not enough eggs are available to fill a machine, but cannot be said to be ideal because a developing embryo requires varying conditions according to age.

Irrespective of the incubator used the essential requirements are:

1. Correct temperature.

2. Ventilation.; should be a constant, steady flow to allow for the growth of the embryo.

3. Correct level of humidity.

Because of the thickness of the shells the correct level of humidity is vital. In this connection the instructions of the manufacturer of the incubator should be followed.

Note: Before embarking on the hatching of ostrich eggs the person lacking experience should receive training and allowed to operate an incubator with poultry eggs. Basically, except for the period, the process is the same.

Figure 6.2 Ostrich Chicks Hatching

They are able to walk and eat immediately, but are sustained by the yolk of the egg for the first two days. They must be allowed to fill their gizzards with very small stones or flints. After that the eating can begin. It is essential to make sure they have this grit, chick crumbs and chopped lucerne or similar from the second day.

For Caption see opposite

Figure 7.1 A Native feeding Chicks

This is taken from the early days of ostrich farming in South Africa. The taming and general welfare are vital for the first 3 months so individual attention is vital.

7

REARING

GENERAL BACKGROUND

Rearing ostrich chicks requires constant care and attention, especially in a climate which is cold and damp. For this reason the following matters should be noted and where appropriate receive attention :

1. Ostrich chicks grow very rapidly at about 30cm per month, reaching almost full height at 6 months.

2. Food must be nutritious , but a high protein level can lead to very rapid development in the body and subsequent leg weakness problems. Around 15% protein is probably the maximum which should be given; slow and steady maturity should be the aim.

3. Chicks should be kept indoors for the first 3 months, but letting them out for short periods in fine weather from about 8 weeks will get them accustomed to the outdoors before they are released fully on to grass at 3 months.

4. Mortality rate may be very high unless precautions are taken as in (3). Use shavings or other litter , but watch the chicks do not eat it . When put outside it should be on ground which has been treated with lime or other sterilizing agent or the young ostriches will quickly succumb to a variety of diseases. Some kind of land rotation system is advisable, allowing the ground to rest every other year. A mistake made by many farmers is to overstock and continue to use the land without liming or ploughing and growing a new crop of lucerne or other grass.

5. Rearing can be done under an infra–red lamp with the lamp being raised gradually along the lines suggested for rearing chicks. Observe the chicks to ensure they are active and not lying around from heat prostration or huddled together because they are chilled.

6. As well as avoiding rain, frost , snow and dampness the chicks should not be exposed to the full glare of the hot sun.

REARING THE CHICKS

With appropriate care and attention the birds will grow rapidly, but this should not be so quickly that they have weak constitutions. Steady development, with body and legs being in harmony is essential. Provision for exercise should always be present for ostriches are active birds.

Ostrich chicks hatch at 42 days when they are a dappled brown with darker spots usually on throat and neck. The feathers feel rather stiff. In the wild they eat many insects which is the ideal food so the chick crumbs must be easily digestible and after the first week should be adequate in protein (15%) ,but no more. If the body gains weight too rapidly the legs may give way and in extreme cases the young birds will have to be killed.

Dampness and keeping in muddy conditions will also tend to produce leg problems; this is why dry, indoor rearing is usually advisable. Do not mix ostriches with other live-stock or there may be a spreading of diseases.

Notes on Rearing

In the treatment of Ostrich chicks it is a case of *many men with many minds*, each swearing by his own particular method. No standard method appears to have been devel-oped and generally accepted.

As stated earlier, chicks hatched in an incubator should be left in the machine until thoroughly dry. The preferred method after then is to keep inside using a mother hen or an infra-red lamp. The choice of brooder depends on how many are being reared and other facilities available. Be-cause of their size ostriches are best reared in a large insu-lated shed, with appropriate ventilation, using fans. Parti-tions can be used to create sections for each batch of chicks. Flexibility is essential so that different ages can be moved along to cooler sections or provision is made for the lamp to be raised each week so that heat is reduced, generally by 5 degrees F.

Within a few days, but only if the weather is favour–able they should be placed outside; preferably under a tree so that they may get a little shade and a little sun alternately. There may be a trap–door system (pop hole) attached to the brooding sheds and the appropriate outlet can be opened when required.

Never expose young Ostrich chicks too much to a hot sun before they get on their legs, and when putting them out let them be in charge of a reliable attendant. At night they must be trained to get back to the brooder. **Young chicks should never be allowed to become chilled or wet.**

In warm climates, after the first few days, they may be placed in covered boxes to sleep and given a little stable litter, or something of the sort, as bedding. This litter should be changed every few days. All sleeping boxes and brooders should be thoroughly disinfected several times during the breeding season.

Writing us on this subject an experienced breeder who uses incubators says:

"Never let the chicks out in the rain, or in the early mornings when they may get wet from the dew; keep them in and give them a green feed until it is dry enough for them to go out. See that all housing is sound and good, well aired and kept clean, give plenty of green food, and let grit and broken bone be always available. Keep the bowels open, as the droppings of the birds are a pretty safe indication as to the health of the chicks. Much depends upon the care and attention given to the chicks during the first month. The first month means much to an Ostrich chick, and it should get a good start if it is to do any good later. As chicks get bigger, they can be left out of the sleeping boxes, and allowed to sleep in a store room or shed. From three months, they may be put into field housing, but shelter they must have if the weather is cold or wet."

Figure 7.2 A Rearer for Ostrich Chicks

This consists of a box in which a lamp or light bulb (red) supplies the heat. It can be modified to suit particular circumstances. This particular model is 45in X 35in X 17in. The chicks would be in a larger room with access to an outside run when weather permits.

Weaning at 3 Months

From three months on, Ostrich chicks can stand a lot, but before that time it does not take much to knock them over.

A very successful breeder, who uses an incubator to hatch his chicks, **believes in natural rearing**. He says: I always try to arrange to have a pair of parent birds to take the young chicks, often shifting the hatching eggs to a sittings pair, removing their eggs to an incubator". However, much depends on how many are to be reared; and remember the ostrich mother may not always be easy to manage.

The chicks should be kept on very short grass or lucerne at first, as they cannot stand wet of any sort, even the the damp from the lucerne in the early morning being too much for them. If you have no parent birds to take the chicks, a keeper must be put in charge.

It is essential to keep the chicks warm for the first week to ten days; a warm, well-ventilated room will do, but it must be kept very clean.

After they are three weeks old they can sleep in the open shed, and very soon in the open air, except in wet weather. Green lucerne is about the best food, with plenty of grit and ad lib feeding of a suitable starter ration, such as Turkey Starter Crumbs. Daily changing of the water is essential.

A farmer had the following comments to make:

"My method of rearing chicks by hand is to put them for the first two days after they are born into small enclosures where they can get plenty of grit, and provide themselves with a set of teeth, but get no food. This lets them get strong on their legs. Then in the morning they are let out to stroll about and pick up grit just anywhere round the farm; the great thing is to keep them moving, as lots of exerise is essential to their growth and health. After breakfast they usually go into the lucerne land for two or three hours, until twelve o'clock, when they are shut up in a cool shed out

of the heat of the sun. Here they have water and grit only until four o'clock, when they go out again for food and exercise until sundown. As a rule they get no grain, yet even so they manage to gorge themselves. My chicks are never kept in a small confined place. Young chicks must always have lots of room. I believe in the free use of disinfectants and whitewash about the boxes and runs. If possible, all chicks should be got out by September. We all try to do it, but how many succeed?"

Losses Amongst Chicks

Up to 3 months the ostrich chicks require great care or the losses will be high. With improved feeding methods this should be avoided and possibly the heavy reliance on lucerne to the exclusion of much else has led to diet deficiencies. An extract from notes taken from a breeder indicates what has occurred in the past:

> **"Although the greatest care is taken of them they die like flies, especially during the first week or fortnight."**

This early mortality of the young chicks has been the subject of considerable study by experts, but no one yet has seemed able to satisfactorily solve the problem. In some cases it is undoubtedly due to the birds being reared on the same ground year after year. Disinfectants have their proper place, but they cannot purify ground which has become foul and disease laden by years of use. **Ground must be purified and sweetened by tillage, or rest.**

The ostrich farmer who rears his chicks on fresh ground each year, or who uses the same ground in alternate years, will be more successful than he who uses the same land continually. It is wise to have a special clean patch of lucerne as the rearing ground each year. An addition to the diet is also advised; a change from lucerne may be given now and then by the use of young green oats, green rape, and kale. Greens they must have. Lucerne is the stand–by or staple, the others for ringing the changes upon. An abundance of grit and other food containing protein must always be given.

Indiscriminate Feeding

One of the main problems with outside chicks is undoubtedly due to the fact that the birds are not provided with sufficient grit, in others it is due to the way in which the chicks gorge themselves with anything and everything they can pick up.

First Aid

If a chick running outdoors eats indigestible objects then an experienced operator may be able to free them. If there is any doubt a veterinary surgeon should be called in for guidance. An ostrich farmer has described the process:

> **What is known as crop–ball or crop–bound is a trouble to which Ostrich chicks are very liable. When a chick is found to be affected its crop should be emptied of its contents, and washed out with clean warm water. The bird should be held firmly by an assistant and the warm water poured down its throat, not a great deal but sufficient to soften the mass in the crop that it begins to move, pour in some more water, continue the kneading with the fingers, and when the contents of the crop are sufficiently softened hold the bird downwards and let the contents of the crop run out of the mouth. It will take some time to accomplish, and a fairly large quantity of water will be used in the attempt, but relief will be given to the chick, and possibly an illness prevented, because diarrheoa invaribly follows crop–binding and in a little while that poor chick will surely die.**

As noted, such treatments must be carried only by experienced stock people, one holding whilst the other performs the necessary treatment. It should be done in the most humane way possible so the bird is not deprived of air.

Figure 7.3 Infra-red Lamp.

This type of lamp has been used successfully for rearing all kinds of livestock including chicks, ducklings, keets, and even piglets.For the ostrich a large lamp and area will be essential.

FEEDING CORRECTLY - AN HISTORICAL NOTE

SPECIAL NOTE:

The need for a protein diet has been noted. Too much reliance on lucerne,"mealies" and grit, along with bone, which was the way of the early ostrich farmers, resulted in high mortality. They had the correct idea, feed a staple food (lucerne), barley meal and bone for protein all of which gave a mixed diet. This was also supplemented by natural food that the ostriches could find on the veldt. Unfortunately, young chicks would find the recipe inadequate and difficult to digest. Moreover, broken bones may carry germs and the danger of infection.

The problems were recognized and attempts were made to produce a balanced ration for the birds, aspecially in the early stages. Thus we have the following description:

In the rearing of Ostrich chicks much depends upon their treatment during the first month. A good start in life means much to the young Ostrich, and more to its owner. It is this first month of an Ostrich chick's life that "Maxco" and "Egfo" ** plays so great a part. By energizing and strengthening the constitution of the chick in its early day's, the special food enables it to withstand, combat, and defeat the ravages of the dreaded tape worm and other internal parasites. The reason so many thousands of young chicks die year by year is because they have no reserve of strength left to draw upon when attacked by these parasities. Therefore, should not every breeder fortify himself and his chicks against these enemies, these dreaded parasites which nullify, not only the efforts of his mind and body, but also diminish and destroy his capital?

Crushed mealies (maize corn) are used by breeders amongst their young stock, but such feeding, whilst very stimulating and provocative of quick growth and feathering, does not build up the constitution in the same way as does a balanced diet . In fact, it has the reverse effect. It pushes growth and feathering at the expense of bodily strength and stamina, encouraging internal parasites. The common complaint of liver disease can also be traced to excess feeding on mealies.

*** A specially formulated food for ostriches, especially for rearing.*

There was very clear recognition that feeding special, balanced food was essential and these were produced under the brand names *Maxco* and *Egfo* for giving the balanced diet necessary. There was specific mention, in the preceding paragraph, that excessive growth of body and feathers could lead to a weakening of the constitution and lead to serious problems.

The Problem:

We have chicks which grow very fast, reaching almost full height at 6 months, and therefore they must have lots of good, nourishing food. Yet if the body weight is allowed to get too large, the legs will not stand the strain, and there will be the serious problem of leg weakness.

The Possible Solution:

Various suggestions have been made to combat this very difficult problem. One has been to restrict the amount of protein given to not more than 15%, even less. Looking at a diet overall it will be appreciated that the feeding of a *partial* diet with protein of 20% may not be excessive if lucerne and other greens are a significant part of the total diet.

Early turning out to pasture, with the consequent high level of exercise, will help to strengthen legs and constitutions. This is what must be practised. Ostriches are outdoor birds and no attempt should be made to turn them into creatures of intensive farming.

A high level of calcium is vital in the form of crushed oyster shell and limestone grit. Manufactured foods also contain calcium, but more should be available and taken to ensure strong growth.

Protein comes from many sources. It may be soya bean meal, fish meal, meat and bone meal, milk powder, dried yeast and other. Any protein from animals must have been properly treated to ensure that there is no danger of spreading disease. Food from animal food manufacturers will have been "sterilised" in the appropriate way so there should be no danger.

The provision of vitamins is also essential. Cod liver oil, grass meal (when shortage in the fields) and yellow maize will supplement the Vitamin A which is vital. Vitamin D will be supplied from the sun light and it is for this reason that chicks should be put outdoors as early as possible.

As any poultry farmer knows:

Chicks grow best with the sun on their backs.

8
THE FEATHERS

IMPORTANCE OF FEATHERS

The feathers and their harvesting were originally the main reason for the prosperity of ostrich farming ; when the fashion for feathers declined so did the industry. Moreover, there seems little hope of a revival to the extent of those early days. Public opinion is against the so called exploitation of birds, yet without such commercialization the ostriches cannot be kept. In fact, of course, provided the feathers are taken by humane methods, described later, the birds feel no pain or suffering.

Nature of the feathers

The ostrich feather, being from a flightless bird, has barbs which are evenly balanced at each side of the quill. Moreover, the barbs are quite soft so they have many possible uses. A comparison of different types of feathers may be seen from Fig. 8.1 which shows feathers from different birds. These have been reduced in size by approximately 50% and are reproduced for the purpose of showing the differences in formation.

In actual length achieved the ostrich has obviously much larger plumes, the longest feathers being known to be over two feet in length and 7ins. wide. The strain of ostrich and its location makes a difference. Those from South Africa were regarded as the best, but not always as soft as from

Figure 8.1 Feathers Compared

Top: **Flight feather of pigeon with stiff vane for flying.**
Second: **Under wing covert of Great Blue Heron.**
Third: **Wing Covert of Owl (downy edge for noisless flight).**
Bottom: **Ostrich -- completely downy for no flight necessary.**

some other locations. In the early days of ostrich farming the merchants could recognize the originating country of the feathers, whether Egypt, Tripoli, Morocco. Senegal or South Africa. Obviously, many of the feathers would come from wild birds so the conditions under which they lived would influence the condition. Those fully domesticated can have the conditions modified to suit top quality feathers, the climate being the main variable factor.

TERMINOLOGY FOR BIRDS

The ostrich farmer has developed a terminology to distinguish the different stages for plucking feathers, thus:

1. **Chicks** -- birds which still have their original feathers; ie, up to about 6 – 7 months old.
2. **Young Birds** -- Up to a year old.
3. **Yearling Birds** -- show new quills; cocks should have some black feathers and should have white on legs and beak.
4. **Two Year Old Birds** -- cocks will have adult feathers; black body and hens a drab grey.
5. **Three Year Old Birds** -- now fully feathered with adult plumage, but the birds not yet fully matured. Cocks will start to be red at the front of legs and on the beak.
6. **Four Year Old Birds** -- now matured and ready to breed with the cocks showing pink on the legs, and on the back sinews and at the front, red .

Classification of the Feathers

The feathers are graded into classes as follows:

1. **Whites (Male) .**
2. **Whites (female).**
3. **Mixed Colours ('Byocks').**
4. **Tail ('Boos').**
5. **Immatures ('Spadonas').**
6. **Black or Drab (long feathers on wing near body for male and female respectively)**

The White ' Superiors' would fetch more than four times as much as the Boos and other inferior grades. This was for the fashion industry and therefore there would not be such a marked differential when used for industrial or other purposes.

Because of the great difference in value between the black and white top quality plumage many feathers were bleached or specially treated and then dyed pink, blue or other desirable colour.Whether such practices will become worthwhile depends on the development of different uses for the feathers.

Prizes for Feathers

Such was the interest in the quality of the feathers that shows were held. These indicated what progress could be made by selection and proper feeding. An example of prime white feathers is shown in Fig. 8.2 which were prize–winners in their day.

HARVESTING THE FEATHERS

The feathers may be harvested in a variety of ways and this aspect is now examined. Plucking, taking quill and feather together, is cruel and harmful and therefore the harvesting should be done in two stages:

1. Cutting off the feather at the base leaving the quill intact.

2. Plucking the quill at the correct time; ie, when the smallest loss of blood will occur (explained below).

Even then there is much to be said for limiting the harvesting to the main or largest wing and tail feathers, leaving the remaining feathers on any living bird*. Then only if birds are killed or die can all feathers can be taken. An adult bird should yield around 1lb of these feathers per annum.

*** This follows the recommendation of the RSPCA in the booklet *Welfare standards for the humane farming of ostriches in the United Kingdom.***

Figure 8.2 Ostrich Feathers

Prime feathers taken from the wing; they correspond with the flight feathers from flying birds.

TAKING THE FEATHERS.

The feathers are taken from about 7 months of age. This may be done outside whilst one attendant holds the bird by the neck or inside when the birds are driven in and gently held whilst the "plucking" is carried out. Some farmers in the past have built a special stand into which birds can be driven for the feather–taking to take place. The important aspect is for the ostriches to be tamed from an early age and not ill treated in any way so that they do not fear the process.

The best way of understanding what is done is to describe the way the harvesting has been tackled by ostrich farmers.

Case Study 1

The whole flock of 70 ostriches were driven into the barn. A bird was selected in the flock and held by the neck – – she could not move much anyway because of the crowd– ing–– and the process was started. The best feathers were selected and the second stockman armed with a curved and sharp knife cut off the feathers near the skin, but leaving the base of the quill quite intact. This was done without any pain or discomfort to the birds.

In about 4 – 6 weeks, after examination of the quill stumps left, these were removed. It is important for the skin to be pressed back after the stump is removed.

This way only the best feathers are selected and the birds feel no ill effects. On the other hand, if a **complete plucking** had been attempted, the birds might suffer ill ef– fects and they may suffer from fever and be attacked by parasites where the new quills had been removed.

Case Study 2

When the chicks are six months old the first white feathers are taken, these are known as ***spads***. They are clipped, the quills being drawn at eight–and–a–half to nine months. No other feathers should be taken at this age, in fact they are worthless commercially, and should be left to keep the chick warm. If the chicks have not grown very well from any cause, such as worms or other ailments, or because the birds have grown very large feathers, they may not be ripe, and may require longer time before being clipped, in like manner the quilling will be delayed. The chicks should be looked through every week or ten days, so as to clip, and more especially to quill, just at right time. It often happens that chicks out of the same hatch will not all ripen their feathers together at the same time.

Before the chicks are quilled they should be carefully examined to see if they are fit and ready for the operation, as a mistake at this time may be followed by serious consequences. If the quilling takes place at eight–and–a–half to nine months you will then get your first feathers at fifteen months. In examining the birds see if the soft thin skin on the quill has worn off up to the socket. If it has then you know that the quill has ripened and is fit to pull. Should it happen, however, that you do not feel quite positive, draw one of the quills; if it is quite dry and clean, then you can quill your chicks, but if there is any mark, or stain of blood upon it you must let the birds run a bit longer. It may be they only need a few days, it may be a fortnight but don't waste time, examine the chicks frequently, as the time is precious, the subsequent crop depending upon the first quilling. If the quilling has been left too long, the quill will show a new bluish growth at the bottom; when this is seen out must come all the quills at once.

The tail feathers and the two rows of **drabs** immediately above the **spad** sockets, and extending from the top of the wing up as far as the elbow, should be pulled at the same time as the chicks are quilled. When quilling the chicks the greatest care must be used; there must be no rough handling. To prevent injury to the sockets place the thumb and forefinger of the left hand on the flesh round the socket, and as you draw the quill with the right hand press the flesh down with the other. Never quill chicks during cold weather, as at such time there is not much force in the system and the feathers do not start their growth evenly, which means serious loss in both quanity and quality at the next clipping. It is a well known fact that feathers starting out singly get barred and spoilt. Many a good bird has been spoilt by being quilled in cold weather.

After the chicks have been quilled they should be given the best of food, so as to give the new feathers a good start. Pellets, grain and lucerne are all essential. This will keep them vigorous and ensure a good clipping. The birds should have also have plenty of grit and protein–rich food given to them, and should it happen that the grass is not in good condition or there is no lucerne paddock, then they should be fed with green food of some kind twice a day.

Regularity in plucking and clipping has much to do with successful ostrich farming; therefore breeders should keep a register of all major processes, and know from it when the times should come again. When examining the old birds to see if they are ready for clipping you should lift the wings and look well at the butts of the quills. If they are dry then the feather is ripe and fit to cut, but if the quills still show blood then the birds should be allowed to run a little while longer. Premature cutting, when the plumes are still green, means there is a loss in the returns expected. There is

Figure 8.3 An old photograph showing an ostrich being plucked.

In this case the bird has been isolated from the flock and a bag placed over his head to keep him calm. The attendants hold him and pluck the feathers required. These days an enclosure or plucking yard would be used with a platform to reach each bird as it is brought round by a stockman to the appropriate position.

a loss in weight, which means smaller monetary returns, and the bird loses a quantity of blood, which fact may have a most derogatory effect upon the next clipping. Further, birds whose plumes are cut green do not last so long as those in which the feather is allowed to ripen properly. Every breeder should try and regulate his quilling so that the feathers grow in the summer months when there is no inclement weather to affect their growth and they terminate in the winter, giving a nice bright finish combined with great length, width and weight.

Return from Feathers

No ostrich farmer can survive on feathers alone. Unless there is a change in fashion the price of feathers will not make the operation viable by itself. As noted, an adult bird will produce about 1 lb. of good quality feathers per annum. The most valuable are the twelve large feathers from each wing. These may be sold for decorative or fashion uses. At a price of say £3 each this represents £72 and the remainder of the feathers would possibly fetch about £20, but these figures it must be emphasized are estimates and may be more or less depending upon the opportunities which are developed by those in the industry and others who are in some way concerned with marketing its products. The number of adult ostriches kept times the £92 will give a rough guide to what can be expected from this source.

Footnote: In recent times old ostrich feather fans have been seen on the market , in antique and 'junk' shops and actually appear to sell at around £30 to £50 so there may be a market in such products.

9

THE EGG

THE LARGEST EGG

As noted earlier the ostrich egg is the largest laid by any bird. It is around 1,400 grammes (0ver 3lb) and measures 15cm X 13cm (6in X 5in.). Around 12 to 17 eggs are laid in a clutch and if these are taken away each hen may lay up to 100 eggs.

A comparison with other eggs will show what a massive feat it is for a single bird to produce such an egg. Moreover, the food and calcium intake has to be enormous.The visual comparison can be seen from Fig. 9.1 which illustrates, side by side. eggs from an ostrich, cassowary, hummingbird and domesticated hen.

Food Value

The food value of the ostrich egg is also high and comprises of around 53% albumen, 33% yolk and 14% shell. In this it comes very near to the fowl, and turkey.

The taste of the ostrich egg also comes up to expectations. In tests carried out and recorded some years ago it was found that on a scale from 1 to 10 (highest or ideal) the ostrich came out at 7.3 compared with the domestic fowl of 8.7. The domesticated duck was 7.1 and the goose 7.1. The pheasant, pigeon and partridge came out with similar figures. (Recorded in *Functional Anatomy of Birds* , A N Worden, nd)

Figure 9.1 Eggs Compared
Ostrich, Cassowary, (back);
Hummingbird and Hen eggs (front)

The grade of below 8 was given to those eggs with a slightly unusual or strong flavour, although quite acceptable to the palate. Thus it can be seen that once the taste has been accepted by the palate there is no reason why ostrich eggs should not be part of a normal diet. They are certainly eaten in South Africa.

Shape of the Egg

As noted, the yellowish white eggs are very large. In shape they are ovoid, but definitely more rounded than a hen egg. Eggs are usually divided into five different shapes:

Ovoid, spherical, elliptical, biconical and conical.

(See Fig 9.3)

The ostrich egg and hen egg is generally the ovoid type, but the hen egg may tend towards elliptical.

Use of the Egg

The food value of the egg has been noted and in developing countries could be a great source of protein. In countries not accustomed to the taste or not by tradition accustomed to eat such large eggs there is a need to educate people on their use provided the effort can be justified. We have to ask ourselves whether the ostrich egg, if produced in reasonable quantities, can compete successfully with the domestic fowl. Possibly if treated as a gourmet food the answer is ' yes', but not for normal domesticated use.

There are bound to be surplus eggs which cannot be incubated so a market must be found. In addition, eggs which are 'clear' and therefore do not develop, may be used for animal foods or similar outlets.

The main source of revenue may be from the use of the

	Weight of egg (grammes)	Percentage proportion made up of: Albumen	Yolk	Shell
PRECOCIAL SPECIES:				
Ostrich	1400	53·4	32·5	14·1
Emu	710	52·2	35·0	12·8
Goose	200	52·5	35·1	12·4
Turkey	85	55·9	32·3	11·8
Duck	80	52·6	35·4	12·0
Fowl	58	55·8	31·9	12·3
Guinea Fowl	40	52·3	35·1	12·6
Ring-necked Pheasant ..	32	53·1	36·3	10·6
Partridge	18	50·8	37·0	12·2
Plover	15	50·7	40·8	8·5
ALTRICIAL SPECIES:				
Golden Eagle	140	78·6	12·0	9·4
Buzzard	60	76·8	14·0	9·2
Dove	22	72·4	18·1	9·5
Pigeon	17	74·0	17·9	8·1
Jay	8·5	68·1	26·6	5·3
Starling	7·0	78·6	14·3	7·1
Robin	2·5	70·3	24·2	5·5
Hedge Sparrow	2·0	72·5	21·6	5·9
Gold-crested Wren ..	1·0	71·0	24·1	4·9
Humming-bird	0·5	69·7	25·3	5·0

Figure 9.2 Comparative Proportions of Albumen, Yolk and Shell in different Eggs.

Source: *The Avian Egg*, Ramanoff & Ramanoff

Quoted by Worden A N, ibid

egg as a whole or in halves (contents therefore utilized) and carved or decorated. Many examples can be seen on market stalls where the eggs have been turned into works of art. The shell is almost 2 mm thick so it has great strength and capable of being used for many purposes.

Commercial Possibilities

The commercial possibilities for the egg are tremendous. If on average around 60 eggs can be obtained per annum from each hen the potential is enormous. From the sale of hatching eggs, chicks, eggs for eating or for art work the total should add up to a considerable sum, dependent on the size of the holding.

Figure 9.4 Nest and Eggs in an outdoor situation

This situation is best avoided by training birds to nest in some form of hut or shelter.

10

OTHER POSSIBLE PRODUCTS

COMMERCIAL POSSIBILITIES

If commercial ostrich farming is to be a success then some attempt must be made to utilize to the full all the possible 'products' which might be derived from the farming operation. In the earlier parts of the book the main possibilities were examined and in the preceding two chapters the sale of feathers and eggs were examined. It now remains to look at some of the other by–products.

They are as follows:

1. **Leather from the skins.**
2. **Meat** by killing birds which are not up to standard for breeding. Strong, broad and vigorous birds are required for breeding , not narrow, hunched up specimens which may be quite healthy, but just not good enough for breeding with.
3. **Manure** from droppings. This is a potential which has not been developed, but should be feasible provided it is stored and left to mature. The ostrich houses will require peat, shavings or short (cut) straw to absorb moisture.

Leather

The leather from the skin of the ostrich, which is the quality of 'kid', can be used for making a wide variety of products such as wallets, handbags, shoes, and cases of various types;this potential market has to be developed.Also the means of tanning and selling to a manufacturer must be taken care of at an early stage because a skin will quickly become ruined unless dealt with speedily.

Meat Products

The meat from the ostrich is regarded as a great delicacy and, as a result, can command the same sort of prices as top quality Scottish steak. Moreover, because of its low protein and cholesterol levels, with appropriate publicity it could be a top level seller. The ostrich farmer refers to this meat as 'volaise'.

The ostrich should be killed at an age when the meat has developed sufficiently to be full of natural juices and taste, yet not too old or the meat will be tough. A bird which is between a year and 18 months is likely to be the optimum age with stock which is not saleable to others as stock birds. Obviously the latter would be more profitable and, in the absence of some type of restrictive policy, should be sold for that purpose rather than kill them.

The yield will be around 80 lb. of lean meat which should sell on the market at a high price; direct to restaurants possibly as high as £8 per pound, but on the general market, especially to a dealer oniy half that figure would be feasible.

Practical Difficulties

One of the major practical difficulties with this end of the market -- disposing of stock for meat or skins is how to cope with killing. Ostriches are very large, strong birds and anyone who has tried to kill a goose or turkey will know how difficult this process can be. Shooting, electrocution, amputation and cutting the throat are all possibilities, but with health regulations it is a process not to be encouraged.

With cattle, pigs, sheep and other livestock the proce–

dures are well known and easy to follow; there is usually a local abbattoir which can take on the responsibility. With ostriches there is difficulty with transportation and the local abbattoir will probably not be able to cope.

In fact, the RSPCA * have stated quite categorically that because of the unsuitability of present facilities an on-farm facility or mobile killing unit appears appropriate. This seems a sensible approach until some better solution has been found.

WASTAGE PROBLEMS

In case a would-be-farmer gets carried away with euphoria on prospects, it must be emphasized that there are possible losses and wastage at all stages. Many chicks do not reach maturity and those that do survive are not all top-class breeding birds or for selling at very high prices. Various statistics have been produced and the following estimates give some idea of the wastage rate:

1. **Breeding stock**..........17% of chicks develop into top breeding stock.
2. **Feather Producers**.........50% will be retained for producing feathers.
3. **Disposals**...........33% of adult birds will not be up to standard for breeding or for feather production and therefore have to be culled to build up a worthwhile flock.

Because of this analysis the ostrich farmer must develop all sources of revenue.

---

* ***Welfare standards, etc*. ibid.**

Figure 11.1 Ostrich carrying native on back

As noted later the ostrich is not suitable for riding although some farms in South Africa do have demonstrations as a tourist attraction. It is dangerous and cruel to the birds.

11

ODD NOTES ON MANAGEMENT

HEALTH PROBLEMS

If there are serious problems such as birds dying, losing weight, breathing problems or other signs which indicate that birds are suffering from serious diseases then a veterinary surgeon should be called in. The notes which follow indicate some of the matters which have been present in the past and therefore should be used as a guide to these normal problems which will be of a minor nature if treated on time.

Ticks

Ticks are tiny parasites with 8 legs which suck the blood from the host and cannot be moved by pulling off or the skin of the ostrich will be damaged. Various dusting powders are available for killing them. They may to some extent be prevented if when the chicks are a day old their heads are rubbed with mixture of equal parts of liquid paraffin and olive oil, or paraffin and linseed oil. Sulphur ointment is an alternative. This may be repeated at intervals of a few days. Ticks are indeed most troublesome if allowed to get a on to the chicks. Should it happen that ticks are found attaching to the head, or inside the ear, as they sometimes do, they may be dislodged by rubbing them with a drop of paraffin. They should never be pulled off, as that leaves a sore spot which often causes a lot of pain and trouble. Some breeders when they find them cut off the body of the ticks, leaving the head to fall away of its own accord, or burn off

Figure 11.2 Ostriches at....

the Water Hole

with a lighted cigarette being careful not to damage the ostrich.

Ash and sand in a dust bath are needed for the chicks to roll in and so prevent them from becoming infested with vermin. Should chicks be found with vermin, a little sulphur dusted in the feathers will help to rid them. In bad cases the birds may be bathed will effectively cleanse the birds from vermin, and will not injure the plumage in any way. Birds should not be given this bath within a month of clipping and care must be taken after the birds have had the bath that they do not go out and roll in sand or dust.

The most critical period in the life or an ostrich is that between one year three months and two years. During these nine months the greatest care must be taken of them. Should it happen that the bird gets into low condition during this period when they change colour, life is apt to prove very fleeting. Therefore, birds which are looking hollow in the sides and prominent in the backbone must be fed up with good nourishing food.

It is a good plan to look the flock over every week, and then the bad doers are easily sorted out. They should be given **ad lib** feeding of growers' pellets as well as lucerne, chopped mangolds, green rape, green oats or any other green food obtainable should be given to them.

Worms

Worms are a source of great trouble to ostrich breed–ers, but we may say that strong, healthy chicks do not give so much trouble with worms as do those who are not so well reared, and this is where the value of those foods come in. Birds who are reared on pellets and lucerne have better nourished bodies and stronger constitutions than those which are not so fed. The first signs of worm trouble are the small white nits which show in the droppings. These are the eggs of the tapeworm, and unless immediate action is taken great trouble will ensue. Immediately the nits are seen the chicks should be dosed.

The chicks should be shut up in a shed, and no food should be given for twelve hours. If they are fed and shut in at night they may be dosed in the morning, which is the best time to dose them, as the effect of the dose may be seen through the day. There are drugs available which would be suitable for worm eradication and a veterinary supply shop or vet. would be able to recommend something suitable.

Lice

Lice can be troublesome and the birds must be watched for any signs of irritation. The answer is to provide a dust bath and at regular intervals to rub sulphur ointment under the wings or near the vent so that any lice are quickly killed. Any clusters of eggs should be removed by pulling out the affected feathers and then rubbing the spot with the ointment.

An Ostrich Dip

On farms in South Africa a **Dip** into a tank of 7ft wide and 40 ft long is a frequent practice. The birds are dipped into the water and sulphur (or other suitable mixture) is added to a consistency which will kill any lice and discourage flies. This is an operation which needs organizing very carefully so that birds are not injured in any way.

Sheep–dip fluid may also be suitable, but care must be taken to ensure that the mixture is not too strong.

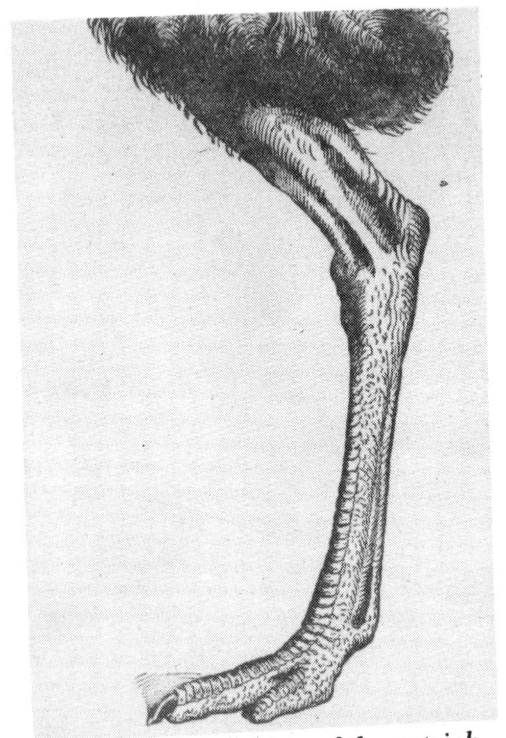

Figure 11.3 The leg of the ostrich.
This powerful limb allows the ostrich to travel at great speed, but also supplies a weapon when necessary.

Figure 11.4 Ostrich drawing a cart
A practice not to be recommended.

TREATMENT OF OSTRICHES

For maximum production and to ensure the safety of stockkeepers and others it is necessary to treat all ostriches with due respect. Generally they are placid creatures who will live in harmony with people, but if they are to be managed properly, bred from, have their feathers plucked and other essential tasks the birds must trust their keepers.

A few rules should ensure that the required harmony prevails:

1. From birth birds should be handled and hand fed so they become tame and the 'imprinting' process is established.
2. Establish regular routines for feeding, cleaning out, changing the bedding and other chores.
3. Ensure that fencing, buildings and equipment are safe and ensure there are no escapes. They constitute a dangerous hazard on the public highway and may bet killed.
4. Do not allow strangers into enclosures unless accompanied and any visits should be as few as possible and conducted in an orderly and quiet fashion.
5. Do not overcrowd the birds.
6. Give good quality food and remember that ostriches are grazing birds so they should not be deprived of grass.

7. Do not indulge in 'horseplay' or use the ostrich for riding or carting or other menial tasks. The ostrich is a very powerful creature with extraordinary legs which allow him to kick with great force and gallop at great speed. The control of an ostrich whilst on his back or whilst pulling a cart would be quite inadequate. In addition, ostriches are not intended to be beasts of burden and there is very little experience of coping with a frightened or angry ostrich on the gallop.

Ostrich farming is a serious business which requires individuals who are not afraid of handling the birds and who are prepared to be resourceful in all aspects of management.

WILL OSTRICH FARMING BE VIABLE ?

The question which must inevitably be asked is how viable will ostrich farming turn out. If a farmer has enough capital to invest in a long–term project there seems little doubt that it can succeed. However, it does not appear to be the type of farming which will produce immediate results. The reader has only to consider the periods involved in growing stock to breeding age (3 years) and then waiting for the offspring to mature to see that there will be a development period of a few years for profitabilty and cash flow to be satisfactory.

There is therefore a strong case for running an ostrich farm with other live–stock which will be compatible with ostriches. Cattle, sheep, goats, ducks and geese are all possibilities, but we must be sure that diseases caught by one type will not be transmitted to the other. Fortunately, ostriches are very healthy creatures so no serious problems should arise from them.

BIBLIOGRAPHY

Many modern books were used, but unfortunately few modern titles are available which deal specicifically with Ostrich Farming.

Beebe C W, *The Bird*, Hy Holt, Ny.

Bertram Brian, *Welfare standards for the humane farming of ostriches in the United Kingdom*, RSPCA, Horsham, West Sussex.

Douglass A, *Ostrich Farming*, Cassell, SA.

Hocking A ,South African Farming, Macdonald, SA , 1975.

Mosenthal J de, *Ostriches and Ostrich Farming*, Trubner & Co, London, 1877.

Ramanoff & Ramanoff, *The Avian Egg*

Worden A N , *Functional Anatomy of Birds*, Cage Birds, nd.

***Ostriches & Incubation*, a booklet issued by Hearsons who were large manufacturers of incubators at the turn of the century.**

***Poultry World*, The journal of poultry farming in the UK.**

INDEX